# Contents

# Acknowledgements

The authors and publisher would like to thank the following individuals and organisations for permission to reproduce photographs:

Construction Photography / DIY Photolibrary 33, 159; Construction Photography / Paul McMullin 49; Construction Photography / Xavier de Canto 25; Corbis / Creasource 31; Corbis / Martin Meyer / Zefa 37; Creatas 138; Getty Images / PhotoDisc 15; Getty Images / PhotoDisc 139; iStockPhoto.com / George Green 214; iStockPhoto.com / Marco Prandina 199; Jupiter Images / Photos.com 121 (bottom); Pearson Education / Gareth Boden 3, 109 (left), 109 (right), 112, 113 (top left, top right, bottom left, bottom right), 114, 120 (top left, bottom right), 121 (top left), 158; Pearson Education / Ian Wedgewood 175, 176, 202, 204, 219, 220 (top and middle); Pearson Education / Jules Selmes 72; Philip Parkhouse 144; Photographers Direct / Anthony Hatley 191; Photographers Direct / Bjorn Beheydt 28; Photographers Direct / Dave Armstrong 174 (right); Photographers Direct / David Griffiths 26, 121 (top right); Photographers Direct / Jim Worlding 173, 174 (left); Photographers Direct / John Gaffen 179; Photographers Direct / Kevin Lockhart 220 (bottom); Photographers Direct / Robert Clare 246; Science Photo Library / Garry Watson 8 (left); Science Photo Library / Scott Camazie 16 (bottom); Shutterstock / K.Jakubowska 221; Shutterstock / David Hughes 170; Shutterstock / David Lee 148; Shutterstock / Stavklem 167; Topham Picturepoint 8 (middle and right); Construction Photography / Grant Smith 13.

# Introduction

This book has been written based on a concept used within Carillion Training Centres for many years. That concept is about providing learners with the necessary information they need to support their studies and at the same time ensuring that it is presented in a style which they find both manageable and relevant.

The content of this book has been put together by a team of instructors, each of whom have a wealth of knowledge and experience in both training for NVQs and Technical Certificates and their trade.

This book has been produced to help the learner build a sound knowledge and understanding of all aspects of the NVQ and Technical Certificate requirements associated with their trade. It has also been designed to provide assistance when revising for Technical Certificate end tests and NVQ job knowledge tests.

Each chapter of this book relates closely to a particular unit of the NVQ or Technical Certificate and aims to provide just the right level of information needed to form the required knowledge and understanding of that subject area.

This book builds on the basic information provided by the Level 2 book, providing more specific terminology and in-depth information about the tools, materials and methods of work required to enable you to complete work activities effectively and productively. Upon completion of your studies, this book will remain a valuable source of information and support when carrying out your work activities.

For further information on how the content of this student book matches to the unit requirements of the NVQ level 3 Diploma in Bricklaying, please visit www.heinemann.co.uk and follow the FE and Vocational link, followed by the Construction link, where a detailed mapping document is available for download.

# How this book can help you

You will discover the following features throughout this book, each of which has been designed and written to increase and improve your knowledge and understanding.

- **Photographs** – identify a tool or material or will help you to follow a step-by-step procedure.

- **Illustrations** – give you more information about a concept or procedure.

- **Definition** – new or difficult words are picked out in bold in the text and defined in the margin.

- **Remember** – highlight key concepts or facts.

- **Safety tip** – guidance to help you work safely.

- **Did you know?** – interesting facts about the building trade.

- **Find out** – short activities designed to lead you to find further information and gain better understanding of a topic area.

- **Activity** – small tasks designed to test your understanding.

- **FAQs** – frequently asked questions together with informative answers from the experts.

- **Knowledge refresher** – questions to test your knowledge and recall of a topic.

- **What would you do?** – real-life situations designed to make you think about what you would do. (Answers can be found on the Tutor Resource Disk that accompanies this book.)

- **Glossary** – contains definitions of all the **bold** words and phrases found in the text. A great quick reference tool.

# chapter 1

# Health and safety

## OVERVIEW

The construction industry is the largest industry in the UK – and the most dangerous. In the past 25 years, almost 3000 people have died from injuries received carrying out construction work; many more have been seriously injured or made ill.

Thankfully, there has been a slight reduction over the last few years: according to the Health and Safety Executive (HSE), 79 people died in 2006/07 compared to 72 people in 2007/08. This minor reduction is due to increased regulations and improved training and awareness. Health and safety training is now a major part of any apprenticeship.

Level 2 gave a good grounding in health and safety, and informed you of what you need to know and do. This Level 3 book will refresh the main points and give you a more comprehensive insight into health and safety in the construction industry.

This chapter will cover:

- health and safety legislation
- health and welfare
- hazards, emergencies and accidents
- risk assessments.

# Health and safety legislation

While at work, whatever your location or type of work, you need to be aware that there is important **legislation** you must comply with. Health and safety legislation is there not just to protect you, but also states what you must and must not do to ensure that no workers are placed in a situation **hazardous** to themselves or others. Each piece of legislation covers your own responsibilities as an employee and those of your employer – it is vital that you are aware of both.

## What is legislation?

Legislation means a law or set of laws passed by Parliament, often called an Act. There are hundreds of Acts covering all manner of work from hairdressing to construction. Each Act states the duties of the **employer** and **employee**. If an employer or employee does something they shouldn't – or doesn't do something they should – they can end up in court and be fined or even imprisoned.

## Approved Code of Practice (ACoP), guidance notes and safety policies

As well as Acts, there are two sorts of codes of practice and guidance notes: those produced by the **Health and Safety Executive (HSE)**, and those created by companies themselves. Most large construction companies – and many smaller ones – have their own guidance notes, which go further than health and safety law. For example, the law states that everyone must wear safety boots in a hazardous area, but a company's code may state that everyone must wear safety boots at all times. This is called taking a **proactive** approach, rather than a **reactive** one.

Most companies have some form of **safety policy** outlining the company's commitment and stating what they plan to do to ensure that all work is carried out as safely as possible. As an employee, you should make sure you understand the company's safety policy as well as their codes of practice. If you act against company policy you may not be prosecuted in court, but you could still be disciplined by the company or even fired.

If you are acting as a supervisor, you will need to ensure that staff you are supervising understand the safety policy too. The safety policy may even require you to take on further responsibilities as a supervisor, such as running safety drills and checks: if so, you will need to understand what is involved in these and ask for any necessary support or training from your employer.

## Definition

**Legislation** – laws or the making of laws

**Hazardous** – dangerous or unsafe

## Definition

**Health and Safety Executive (HSE)** – government organisation that enforces health and safety law in the UK

**Proactive** – acting in advance, before something happens (such as an accident)

**Reactive** – acting after something happens, in response to it

## Find out

Health and safety regulations are constantly being updated and amended. Log on to the HSE website (www.hse.gov.uk/construction) to see what recent updates there have been to the different regulations.

# Health and safety legislation you need to be aware of

There are some 20 pieces of legislation you will need to be aware of, each of which sets out requirements for employers and often employees. One phrase often comes up here – 'so far as is reasonably practicable'. This means that health and safety must be adhered to at all times, but must take a common sense, practical approach.

For example, the Health and Safety at Work Act 1974 (HASAWA) states that an employer must *so far as is reasonably practicable* ensure that a safe place of work is provided. Yet employers are not expected to do everything they can to protect their staff from lightning strikes, as there is only a 1 in 800,000 chance of this occurring – this would not be reasonable!

We will now look at the regulations that will affect you most.

## The Health and Safety at Work Act 1974

The Health and Safety at Work Act was first introduced on 31 July 1974. It is described as follows:

> ' … an act to make further provisions for securing the health, safety and welfare of persons at work, for protecting others against risks to health and safety in connection with the activities of persons at work, for controlling the keeping and use and preventing the unlawful acquisition, possession and use of dangerous substances, and for controlling certain emissions into the atmosphere; to make further provision with respect to the employment medical advisory services; to amend the law relating to building regulations, and the Building (Scotland) Act 1959; and for connected purposes.'

This is what the law states, but what does it mean to your employer or to you as an employee?

The HASAWA applies to all types and places of work and to employers, employees, the self-employed, sub-contractors and even suppliers. The act is there to protect not only the people at work but also the general public, who may be affected in some way by the work that has been or will be carried out.

The main **objectives** of the health and safety at work act are to:

- ensure the health, safety and welfare of all persons at work
- protect the general public from all work activities

**Activity**

When you reach the end of the qualification, you need to think about what area of work you want to be involved in, and if you wish to be self-employed. Using an area of work you are interested in as an example, as you read through this chapter, write notes on a safety policy for a company you might set up.

The HASAW Act must be displayed at all workplaces

- control the use, handling, storage and transportation of explosives and highly flammable substances

- control the release of noxious or offensive substances into the atmosphere.

To ensure that these objectives are met there are duties for all employers, employees and suppliers.

## Employer's duties

Employers must:

- provide safe **access** and **egress** to and within the work area

- provide and maintain a safe working environment

- provide and maintain plant and machinery that is safe and without risks to health

- provide information, instruction, training and supervision to ensure the health and safety at work of all employees

- ensure safety and the absence of risks to health in connection with the handling, storage and transportation of articles and substances

- have a written safety policy that must be revised and updated regularly, and ensure all employees are aware of it

- involve trade union safety representatives, where appointed, in all matters relating to health and safety

- provide and not charge for **personal protective equipment (PPE)**.

## Employee's duties

The employee must:

- take reasonable care for his/her own health and safety

- take reasonable care for the health and safety of anyone who may be affected by his/her acts or **omissions**

- co-operate with his/her employer or any other person to ensure legal **obligations** are met

- not misuse or interfere with anything provided for their health and safety

- use any equipment and safeguards provided by his/her employer.

Those supervising others will need to make sure that staff are using all safety equipment in the appropriate way, and are taking any necessary steps to ensure that they do not jeopardise their own or others' safety.

Employees cannot be charged for anything that has been done or provided for them to ensure that legal requirements on health and safety are met. The self-employed and sub-contractors have the same duties as employees – and if they have employees of their own, they must obey the duties set down for employers.

### Definition

**Access** – entrance, a way in

**Egress** – exit, a way out

**PPE** – personal protective equipment, such as gloves, a safety harness or goggles

### Definition

**Omission** – something that has not been done or has been missed out

**Obligation** – something you have a duty or a responsibility to do

## Supplier's duties

Persons designing, manufacturing, importing or supplying articles or substances for use at work must ensure that:

- articles are designed and constructed so that they will be safe and without risk to health at all times while they are being used or constructed

- substances will be safe and without risk to health at all times when being used, handled, transported and stored

- tests on articles and substances are carried out as necessary

- adequate information is provided about the use, handling, transporting and storing of articles or substances.

HASAWA, like most of the other acts mentioned, is enforced by the Health and Safety Executive (HSE).  HSE inspectors visit sites and have the power to:

- enter any premises at any reasonable time

- take a police constable with them

- examine and investigate anything on the premises

- take samples

- take possession of any dangerous article or substance

- issue improvement notices giving a company a certain amount of time to sort out a health and safety problem

- issue a **prohibition** notice stopping all work until the site is deemed safe

- **prosecute** people who break the law including employers, employees, self-employed, manufacturers and suppliers.

## *Provision and Use of Work Equipment Regulations 1998 (PUWER)*

These regulations cover all new or existing work equipment – leased, hired or second-hand. They apply in most working environments where the HASAWA applies, including all industrial, offshore and service operations.

PUWER covers starting, stopping, regular use, transport, repair, modification, servicing and cleaning.

Legislation is there to protect employees and the public alike

'Work equipment' includes any machinery, appliance, apparatus or tool, and any assembly of components that are used in non-domestic premises. Dumper trucks, circular saws, ladders, overhead projectors and chisels would all be included, but substances, private cars and structural items all fall outside this definition.

The general duties of the regulations require equipment to be:

- suitable for its intended purpose and only to be used in suitable conditions
- maintained in an efficient state and maintenance records kept
- used, repaired and maintained only by a suitably trained person, when that equipment poses a particular risk
- able to be isolated from all its sources of energy
- constructed or adapted to ensure that maintenance can be carried out without risks to health and safety
- fitted with warnings or warning devices as appropriate.

In addition, the regulations require:

- all personnel to be trained and deemed competent before using any work equipment
- all those who use, supervise or manage work equipment to be suitably trained
- access to any dangerous parts of the machinery to be prevented or controlled
- injury to be prevented from any work equipment that may have a very high or low temperature
- suitable controls to be provided for starting and stopping the work equipment
- suitable emergency stopping systems and braking systems to be fitted to ensure the work equipment is brought to a safe condition as soon as reasonably practicable
- suitable and sufficient lighting to be provided for operating the work equipment.

## Control of Substances Hazardous to Health Regulations 2002

The Control of Substances Hazardous to Health Regulations 2002 (COSHH) state how employees and employers should work with, handle, store, transport and dispose of potentially hazardous substances (substances that might negatively affect your health) including:

- substances used directly in work activities (e.g. adhesives or paints)
- substances generated during work activities (e.g. dust from sanding wood)
- naturally occurring substances (e.g. sand dust)
- biological agents (e.g. bacteria).

Correct labelling and storage of hazardous substances saves lives

These substances can be found in nearly all work environments. All are covered by COSHH regulations except asbestos and lead paint, which have their own regulations.

To comply with COSHH regulations, eight steps must be followed:

**Step 1** Assess the risks to health from hazardous substances used or created by your activities.

**Step 2** Decide what precautions are needed.

**Step 3** Prevent employees from being exposed to any hazardous substances. If prevention is impossible, the risk must be adequately controlled.

**Step 4** Ensure control methods are used and maintained properly.

**Step 5** Monitor the exposure of employees to hazardous substances.

**Step 6** Carry out health **surveillance** to ascertain if any health problems are occurring.

**Step 7** Prepare plans and procedures to deal with accidents such as spillages.

**Step 8** Ensure all employees are properly informed, trained and supervised.

### Safety tip

Not all substances are labelled, and sometimes the label may not match the contents. If you are in any doubt, do not use or touch the substance.

Identifying a substance that may fall under the COSHH regulations is not always easy, but you can ask the supplier or manufacturer for a COSHH data sheet, outlining the risks involved with it. Most substance containers carry a warning sign stating whether the contents are corrosive, harmful, toxic or bad for the environment.

Corrosive          Toxic hazard          Risk of explosion

Common safety signs for corrosive, toxic and harmful materials

### The Personal Protective Equipment at Work Regulations 1992

These regulations, known as PPER, cover all types of PPE, from gloves to breathing apparatus. After doing a risk assessment and once the potential hazards are known, suitable types of PPE can be selected. PPE should be checked prior to issue by a trained and competent person and in line with the manufacturer's instructions. Where required, the employer must provide PPE free of charge along with a suitable and secure place to store it.

The employer must ensure that the employee knows:

- the risks the PPE will avoid or reduce
- its purpose and use
- how to maintain and look after it
- its limitations.

The employee must:

- ensure that they are trained in the use of the PPE prior to use
- use it in line with the employer's instructions
- return it to storage after use
- take care of it, and report any loss or defect to their employer.

**Remember**

PPE must only be used as a last line of defence.

## The Control of Noise at Work Regulations 2005

At some point in your career in construction, you are likely to work in a noisy working environment. These regulations help protect you against the consequences of being exposed to high levels of noise, which can lead to permanent hearing damage.

Damage to hearing has a range of causes, from ear infections to loud noises, but the regulations deal mainly with the latter. Hearing loss can result from one very loud noise lasting only a few seconds, or from relatively loud noise lasting for hours, such as a drill.

The regulations state that the employer must:

Noise doesn't have to be loud to damage your hearing

- assess the risks to the employee from noise at work
- take action to reduce the noise exposure that produces these risks
- provide employees with hearing protection or, if this is impossible, reduce the risk by other methods
- make sure the legal limits on noise exposure are not exceeded
- provide employees with information, instruction and training
- carry out health surveillance where there is a risk to health.

Anyone who is supervising the work of others may be asked to (or may wish to) monitor noise levels in the work area and advise the employer if any problems arise from excessive noise exposure.

## The Work at Height Regulations 2005

In these regulations, 'working at height' covers not only working from scaffolding or other high places, but also working at ground level or below if a person can be injured by falling from that level.

Falls are the biggest cause of death and serious injury in the construction industry, so these regulations make sure that employers do all that they can to reduce the risk of injury or death from working at height.

### Did you know?

Noise is measured in **decibels (dB)**. The average person may notice a rise of 3dB, but with every 3dB rise, the noise is doubled. What may seem like a small rise is actually very significant.

The employer's main duty is to do all that is reasonably practicable to prevent anyone falling. In doing this, the employer must:

- avoid work at height where possible

- use any equipment or safeguards that will prevent falls

- use equipment and any other methods that will minimise the distance and consequences of a fall.

The employer must also ensure that:

- all work at height is properly planned

- weather conditions that can endanger health and safety are taken into account

- those involved in the work are trained and competent

- the place where the work is being done is safe

- equipment is appropriately inspected

- the risks from fragile surfaces are properly controlled

- the risks from falling objects are properly controlled.

As an employee, you must follow any training given to you, report any hazards to your supervisor and use any safety equipment made available to you.

## The Electricity at Work Regulations 1989

These regulations cover any work involving the use of electricity or electrical equipment. An employer has the duty to ensure that the electrical systems their employees come into contact with are safe and regularly maintained. They must also have done everything the law states to reduce the risk of their employees coming into contact with live electrical currents.

## The Manual Handling Operations Regulations 1992

More than a third of all over-three-day injuries reported to the HSE are caused by manual handling – the transporting or supporting of loads by hand or bodily force. These regulations cover all work activities in which a person, rather than a machine, does the lifting.

The regulations require employers to:

- **avoid** the need for manual handling, so far is as reasonably practicable

- **assess** the risk of injury from any hazardous manual handling that cannot be avoided

- **reduce** the risk of injury from hazardous manual handling, so far as is reasonably practicable.

The best way for an employer to meet these regulations is to carry out manual handling risk assessments. In a risk assessment, there are four considerations:

- **Load** – is it heavy, sharp-edged, difficult to hold?

- **Individual** – is the individual small, pregnant, in need of training?

- **Task** – does the task require holding goods away from the body, or repetitive twisting?

- **Environment** – is the floor uneven, are there stairs, is it raining?

After the assessment, the situation must be monitored constantly and updated or changed if necessary.

## The Reporting of Injuries, Diseases and Dangerous Occurrences Regulations 1995 (RIDDOR)

Under the Reporting of Injuries, Diseases and Dangerous Occurrences Regulations 1995 (RIDDOR), employers have a duty to report work-related deaths, major injuries, over-three-day injuries, work-related diseases and dangerous occurrences (near miss accidents).

Reporting accidents and ill health at work is a legal requirement. The information reported to the HSE enables it to identify where and how risks arise and to investigate serious accidents, so that advice can be given to prevent any reoccurrences.

Reporting any relevant injury, disease or dangerous occurrence covered by RIDDOR can be done by telephone, online at the HSE website, by e-mail or by post.

## Other acts to be aware of

You should also be aware of the following legislation:

- The Fire Precautions (Workplace) Regulations 1997

- The Fire Precautions Act 1991

- The Highly Flammable Liquids and Liquid Petroleum Gases Regulations 1972

- The Lifting Operations and Lifting Equipment Regulations 1998

- The Construction (Health, Safety and Welfare) Regulations 1996

- The Environmental Protection Act 1990

- The Confined Spaces Regulations 1997

- The Working Time Regulations 1998

- The Health and Safety (First Aid) Regulations 1981

- The Construction (Design and Management) Regulations 1994.

You can find out more at the library or online.

### Find out

Look into the other regulations listed here via the government website www.hse.gov.uk

### Activity

Think of a simple task within your occupation. What regulations would apply to that task? Write down these regulations, then state what your responsibilities would be under each regulation.

## Knowledge refresher

1 What is legislation?

2 What is an approved code of practice?

3 What is the purpose of a safety policy?

4 What does 'so far as is reasonably practicable' mean?

5 Who enforces the health and safety regulation?

6 State three main objectives of the HASAW Act 1974.

7 State the main objective of the Working at Height Regulations.

8 State four duties included in the PUWER regulations.

9 How can an occurrence covered by RIDDOR be reported?

## What would you do?

1 You are about to carry out a task that involves chemicals. The regulations state that risk assessments should be carried out before starting the task. The risk assessments show that expensive measures will need to be put into place if you are to complete the task – and this would mean that you would not make a decent profit. Cheaper options are available but will not offer the same protection. What should you do? What outcomes could there be? What could have been done before getting to this stage?

2 Your employer has asked you and a colleague to work on a scaffold that has not been checked and you think is a bit unsafe. Your colleague, who seems to be on good terms with the boss, says there is no problem, but you raise your concerns with your employer. He ridicules you and replies, 'If you won't do it, I'll find someone who will.' What should you do? What could be the repercussions? What rights do you have as an employee? What obligations does your employer have?

# Health and welfare

As a worker in the construction industry, you will be at constant risk unless you adopt a good health and safety attitude. By following the rules and regulations, and by taking reasonable care of yourself and others – especially where acting as a supervisor – you will become a safe worker and reduce the chance of injuries and accidents. Given the statistics on safety, the supervisor's role is crucial here: few other people will be in a better position to understand the day-to-day work of a site, be in touch with those doing the labour and spot 'danger points' where accidents or ill health could occur.

## The two most common risks to a construction worker

Before reading further, what do you think the two most common risks to a construction worker might be? Think about the industry you are working in and the hazards and risks that exist.

In fact, the most common health and safety risks a construction worker faces are:

- accidents
- ill health.

### *Accidents*

We often hear the saying 'accidents will happen', but in the construction industry, the truth is that most accidents are caused by human error – someone does something they shouldn't or, just as importantly, does not do something they should. Accidents often happen when someone is hurrying, not paying attention, trying to cut corners or costs, or has not received the correct training.

If an accident happens, you or the person it happened to may be lucky enough to escape uninjured. More often, an accident will result in an injury, whether minor (e.g. a cut or a bruise), major (e.g. loss of a limb) or even fatal. The most common causes of fatal accidents in the construction industry are:

- falling from scaffolding
- being hit by falling objects and materials
- falling through fragile roofs
- being hit by forklifts or lorries
- cuts
- infections
- burns
- **electrocution**.

A fall could be fatal so a safety harness should always be worn

### Definition

**Electrocution** – death through coming into contact with an electric current

## *Ill health*

In the construction industry, you will be exposed to substances or situations that may be harmful to your health. Some of these health risks may not be noticeable straight away and it may take years for symptoms to be noticed and recognised.

Ill health can result from:

- exposure to dust (or asbestos fibres) – breathing problems and cancer
- exposure to **solvents** or chemicals – dermatitis and other skin problems
- lifting heavy or difficult loads – back injury and pulled muscles
- exposure to loud noise – hearing problems and deafness
- exposure to sunlight, which can cause skin cancer
- using vibrating tools – **vibration white finger** and other hand problems.

## Substance abuse

'Substance abuse' is a general term that covers drinking alcohol and taking drugs, as well as other substances.

Drinking alcohol is dangerous at work; going to the pub for lunch and having just one drink can lead to slower reflexes and reduced concentration.

Taking drugs or inhaling solvents at work is not only illegal, but is also highly dangerous to you and everyone around you, as reduced concentration can lead to accidents.

Although not a form of abuse as such, taking drugs prescribed by your doctor or even over-the-counter painkillers can be dangerous. Many of these medicines carry warnings such as 'may cause drowsiness' or 'do not operate heavy machinery'. It is better to be safe than sorry, so always ensure you follow any instructions on prescriptions and, if you feel drowsy or unsteady, stop work immediately.

## Staying healthy

As well as watching for hazards, you must also look after yourself and stay healthy.

One of the easiest ways to do this is to wash your hands regularly: this prevents hazardous substances entering your body through ingestion (swallowing). You should always wash your hands after going to the toilet and before eating or drinking.

Other precautions that you can take include the following:

- ensuring that you wear barrier cream to protect yourself from the sun
- using the correct PPE to ensure that your back, arms and legs are sufficiently covered
- drinking only water that is labelled as drinking water.

## Welfare facilities

Welfare facilities are things that an employer must provide to ensure a safe and healthy workplace.

- **Toilets** – The number provided depends on how many people are intending to use them. Males and females can use the same toilet providing the door can be locked from the inside. Toilets should ideally be flushable with water or, if this is not possible, with chemicals.

- **Washing facilities** – Employers must provide a basin large enough for people to wash their hands, face and forearms, with hot and cold running water, soap and a way to dry your hands. Showers may be needed if the work is very dirty or if workers are exposed to toxic or corrosive substances.

- **Drinking water** – A supply of clean drinking water should be available, from a mains-linked tap or bottled water. Mains-linked taps need to be clearly labelled as drinking water; bottled drinking water must be stored where there is no chance of contamination.

- **Storage or dry room** – Every building site must have an area where workers can store clothes not worn on site, such as coats and motorcycle helmets. If this area is to be used as a drying room, adequate heating must be provided.

- **Lunch area** – Every site must have facilities for taking breaks and lunch well away from the work area. There must be shelter from the wind and rain, with heating as required, along with tables and chairs, a kettle or urn and a means of heating food.

Always wash your hands to prevent ingesting hazardous substances

# Hazards, emergencies and accidents

The building industry can be a very dangerous place to work and there are certain hazards that all workers need to be aware of.

The main types of hazards that you will face are:

- falling from height
- tripping
- chemical spills
- burns
- electrical hazards
- fires.

Falling from height and fires have been covered in detail in Level 2, so here we will look at the remaining hazards.

## Tripping

The main cause of tripping is poor housekeeping. Whether working on scaffolding or at ground level, an untidy workplace is an accident waiting to happen. All workplaces should be kept tidy and free of debris. All off-cuts should be put either straight into a skip or, if you are not near a skip, in a wheelbarrow. Not only will this prevent trip hazards, it will also prevent costly clean-up operations at the end of the job and will promote a good professional image.

An untidy work site can present many trip hazards

## Chemical spills

A chemical spill can be anything from a minor inconvenience to a major disaster. Most spills are small and create minimal or no risk. If the material involved is not hazardous, it can be cleaned up by normal operations such as brushing or mopping. However, on some occasions the spill may be on a larger scale and may involve a hazardous material. It is important to know what to do before the spill happens so that remedial action can be prompt, and harmful effects minimised.

Before a hazardous substance is used, a COSHH or risk assessment will have been made, which should include a plan for dealing with a spill. This, in turn, should mean that the materials required for dealing with the spill should be readily available.

## Burns

Burns can occur not only from the obvious source of fire and heat but also from materials such as cement or painter's solvents. Even electricity can cause burns. It is vital when working with any material that you are aware of the hazards it may present and that you take the necessary precautions.

If you receive a burn, or find yourself having to help a colleague who has one, you must act quickly and carefully. Get in touch with a First Aider straight away, and then contact the emergency services.

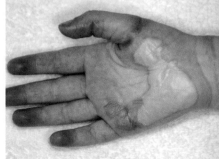

Fire, heat, chemicals and electricity can cause burns

## Electrical hazards

Electricity is a killer. According to the HSE, around 30 workers a year die from electricity-related accidents, with over 1000 more being seriously injured.

One of the main problems with electricity is that it is invisible. You do not even have to be working with an electric tool to be electrocuted: working too close to live overhead cables, plastering a wall with electric sockets, carrying out maintenance work on a floor, or drilling into a wall can all lead to an electric shock.

Electric shocks may not always be fatal: electricity can also cause burns, muscular problems and cardiac (heart) problems. Despite the common perception, the level of voltage is not a direct guide to the level of injury or danger of death: a small shock from static electricity may contain thousands of volts, but has very little current behind it. However, it is generally true that the lower the voltage, the lower the chance of death occurring.

## Household wiring

There are two main types of voltage in use in the UK. These are 230 V and 110 V. The standard UK power supply is 230 V – this is what all the sockets in your house are.

Contained within the wiring there should be three wires: the live and neutral, which carry the alternating current, and the earth wire, which acts as a safety device. The three wires are colour-coded:

- live – brown
- neutral – blue
- earth – yellow and green.

These colours comply with current European colours. Some older properties you work on may have the following colours:

- live – red
- neutral – black
- earth – yellow and green.

230 V has been deemed unsafe on construction sites, so 110 V must be used here. 110 V, identified by a yellow cable and different style of plug, works from a transformer which converts the 230 V to 110 V.

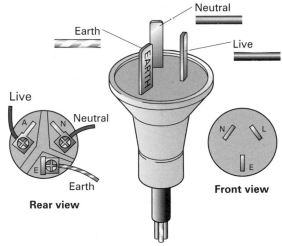

**Figure 1.1** Colour coding of the wires in a 110 V plug

## Dealing with electric shocks

In helping a victim of an electric shock, the first thing you must do is disconnect the power supply, if it is safe to do and will not take long to find – touching the power source may put you in danger.

If the victim is in contact with something portable, such as a drill, try to move it away using a non-conductive object, such as a wooden broom. Time is precious and separating the victim from the source can prove an effective way to speed the process. Do not attempt to touch the affected person until they are free and clear of the supplied power, and don't touch the victim until you are sure the power supply is turned off. Be especially careful in wet areas, such as bathrooms, since water can conduct electricity, and electrocuting yourself is also possible.

A 110 V plug

People 'hung up' in a live current flow may think they are calling out for help but it is likely that no sound will be heard from them. When the muscles contract under household current (most electrocutions happen from house current at home), the person affected will seem to be in a 'locked up' state, unable to move or react to you.

Using a wooden object, swiftly and strongly knock the person free, trying not to injure them, and land them clear of the source. You may lift or remove the item, if it is safe for you to do so, with the same wooden item. This is not recommended on voltages that exceed 500 V. Do not attempt any of this unless you are wearing shoes with rubber or some form of insulated sole: bare or socked feet will allow the current to flow to the ground through your body as well.

### First aid procedures for an electric shock victim

- Check if you are alone. If there are other people around, instruct them to call an ambulance right away.

- Check the victim's breathing, and see if they can respond to you.

- If the area is safe for you to be in, and you have removed the object or have cut off its power supply, shout to the victim to see if they are conscious. At this stage, do not touch them.

- Check once again to see if the area is safe. If you are satisfied that it is safe, start resuscitating the victim if required. If you have no first aid knowledge, call emergency services for an ambulance.

## Emergencies

So far, we have covered most of the emergencies that occur on site, such as accidents and fires, but there are other emergencies that you need to be aware of, such as security alerts and bomb scares.

At your site induction, it should be made perfectly clear to you what you should do in the event of an emergency. You also should be made aware of any sirens or warning noises that accompany each and every type of emergency, such as bomb scares or fire alarms. Some sites may have variations on sirens or emergency procedures, so it is vital that you pay attention and listen to all instructions. If you are unsure, always ask.

## Knowledge refresher

1   What are the two most common risks to construction workers?

2   List three things that can cause ill health, and what health problems they can create.

3   State five welfare facilities that must be available.

4   State the correct colour for 110 V cables/plugs.

5   How should a chemical spill be dealt with?

6   What colour(s) are earth wires in standard 230 V plugs?

## What would you do?

You are inducted onto a new site, but the person hosting the induction does not give very clear instructions. The induction finishes and you are still unsure of what the site rules are or what do to in case of an emergency. What should/would you do?

## Accidents

### Reporting accidents

When an accident occurs, there are certain things that must be done. All accidents need to be reported and recorded in the accident book, and the injured person must report to a trained first aider to receive treatment. Serious accidents must be reported under RIDDOR: these regulations state that your employer must report to the HSE any accident that results in:

- death

- major injury

- an injury that means the injured person is not at work for more than three consecutive days.

### Activity

Working in a group, create a presentation to highlight a type of accident or injury and open a discussion to consider ways of avoiding the accident.

## Report of an Accident, Dangerous Occurrence or Near Miss

Date of incident _____     Time of incident _____

Location of incident _____

**Details of person involved in accident**

Name _____     Date of birth _____     Sex _____

Address _____

_____

_____     Occupation _____

Date off work (if applicable) _____     Date returning to work _____

Nature of injury _____

**Management of injury**
- [ ] First Aid only
- [ ] Advised to see doctor
- [ ] Sent to casualty
- [ ] Admitted to hospital

**Account of accident, dangerous occurrence or near miss**
(Continued on separate sheet if necessary)

**Witnesses to the incident**
(Names, addresses and occupations)

Was the injured person wearing PPE? If yes, what PPE? _____

_____

Signature of person completing form _____

Occupation _____     Date _____

**Figure 1.2** A typical accident book page

## Remember

Health and safety is everyone's duty. If you receive first aid treatment and notice that there are only two plasters left, you should report it to your line manager.

## The accident book

The accident book is completed by the person who had the accident or, if this is not possible, by someone representing the injured person. The accident book will ask for some basic details about the accident, including:

- who was involved
- what happened
- where it happened
- the day and time of the accident
- details of any witnesses to the accident
- the address of the injured person
- what PPE was being worn
- what first aid treatment was given.

As well as reporting accidents, 'near misses' must also be reported. This is because near misses are often the accidents of the future: reporting near misses might identify a problem and can prevent accidents from happening. In this way, a company can try to prevent future accidents, rather than just dealing with the ones that happen.

## First aid

In the unfortunate event of an accident on site, first aid may have to be administered. If there are more than five people on a site, a qualified first aider must be present at all times. On large building sites, there must be several first aiders. During your site induction, you will be made aware of who the first aiders are and where the first aid points are situated. A first aid point must have the relevant first aid equipment to deal with the types of injuries that are likely to occur. However, first aid is only the first step and, in the case of major injuries, the emergency services should be called.

### First aid box

A good first aid box should have plasters, bandages, antiseptic wipes, latex gloves, eye patches, slings, wound dressings and safety pins. Other equipment, such as eye wash stations, must also be available if the work being carried out requires it.

# Risk assessments

You will have noticed that most of the legislation we have looked at requires risk assessments to be carried out. The Management of Health and Safety at Work Regulations 1999 require every employer to make suitable and sufficient assessment of:

- the risks to the health and safety of his/her employees to which they are exposed while at work

- the risks to the health and safety of persons not in his/ her employment arising out of or in connection with his/her work activities.

As a Level 3 candidate, it is vital that you know how to carry out a risk assessment. Often you may be in a position where you are given direct responsibility for this, and the care and attention you take

Even an everyday task like cutting the grass has its own dangers

over it may have a direct impact on the safety of others. You must be aware of the dangers or hazards of any task, and know what can be done to prevent or reduce the risk.

There are five steps in a risk assessment – here we use cutting the grass as an example:

### Step 1 Identify the hazards

When cutting the grass the main hazards are from the blades or cutting the wire, electrocution and any stones that may be thrown up.

### Step 2 Identify who will be at risk

The main person at risk is the user but passers-by may be struck by flying debris.

### Step 3 Calculate the risk from the hazard against the likelihood of an accident taking place

The risks from the hazard are quite high: the blade or wire can remove a finger, electrocution can kill and the flying debris can blind or even kill. The likelihood of an accident happening is

### Did you know?

We all carry out risk assessments hundreds of times a day. For example, every time we boil a kettle, we do a risk assessment without even thinking about it: for example, by checking the kettle isn't too full, or the cable frayed, and by keeping children out of the way.

### Definition

**Making a risk assessment** – measuring the dangers of an activity against the likelihood of accidents taking place

### Activity

Using a fictitious task that you are familiar with, create a risk assessment, showing what the risks are and what measures you could introduce to control them.

medium: you are unlikely to cut yourself on the blades, but the chance of cutting through the cable is medium, and the chance of hitting a stone high.

### Step 4  Introduce measures to reduce the risk

Training can reduce the risks of cutting yourself; training and the use of an **RCD** can reduce the risk of electrocution; and raking the lawn first can reduce the risk of sending up stones.

### Step 5  Monitor the risk

Constantly changing factors mean any risk assessment may have to be modified or even changed completely. In our example, one such factor could be rain.

## FAQ

### What is the difference between being an employee and being a supervisor when it comes to health and safety?

As a supervisor, you need to be aware of the different pieces of legislation and consider them when you are overseeing other people's work. You may be given responsibility to help your employer comply with their part of legislation too.

### How do I find out what safety legislation is relevant to my job?

Ask your employer or contact the HSE at www.hse.gov.uk.

### How do I find my company's safety policy?

Ask your supervisor or employer.

### When do I need to do a risk assessment?

A risk assessment should be carried out if there is any chance of an accident happening. To be on the safe side, you should make a risk assessment before starting each task.

### Do I need to read and understand every regulation?

No. It is part of your employer's duty to ensure that you are aware of what you need to know.

## Knowledge refresher

1  Who should fill in an accident report form?

2  List five pieces of information that should be entered onto an accident report form.

3  Why is it important to report 'near misses'?

4  Name five items that it's a good idea to have in a first aid kit.

5  Briefly explain what a risk assessment is.

6  State why risk assessments should be monitored.

## What would you do?

1  You are a self-employed sub-contractor working on a job when you accidentally cut your finger. The cut is not too deep but may require medical treatment. You put a plaster on it and get back to work, but later on you notice that the bleeding hasn't really stopped and you start to feel light-headed. If you stop work, you won't get paid and could lose out on future work. What do you do? What could the repercussions be for your work? What could the repercussions be for your health?

2  You are asked to do a job and on getting there you notice that the risk assessments have already been done. You quickly scan through them and notice that they are not done for this job but have been based on a previous job. You speak to the supervisor and he states that the job is similar, so the risks should be the same. What do you think?

# chapter 2

# Building documentation

## OVERVIEW

In the construction industry you come across a wide range of documentation, and as a Level 3 apprentice you will encounter different types of documents more frequently. This chapter covers the main building documentation you will see, explaining what each type of documentation is and what it is used for.

The types of documentation covered in this chapter are:

- contract documents
- the Building Regulations
- general site paperwork.

# Contract documents

Contract documents are vital to a construction project. They are created by a team of specialists – the architect, structural engineer, services engineer and quantity surveyor – who first look at the draft of drawings from the architect and client. Just which contract documents this team goes on to produce will vary depending on the size and type of work being done, but will usually include:

- plans and drawings
- specification
- schedules
- bill of quantities
- conditions of contract.

Plans and drawings are covered in Chapter 4, so here we will start with the specifications.

## Specification

A good 'spec' helps avoid confusion when dealing with sub-contractors or suppliers

The specification or 'spec' is a document produced alongside the plans and drawings and is used to show information that cannot be shown on the drawings. Specifications are almost always used, except in the case of very small contracts. A specification should contain:

- **site description** – a brief description of the site including the address
- **restrictions** – what restrictions apply such as working hours or limited access
- **services** – what services are available, what services need to be connected and what type of connection should be used
- **materials description** – including type, sizes, quality, moisture content, etc.
- **workmanship** – including methods of fixing, quality of work and finish.

The specification may also name sub-contractors or suppliers, or give details such as how the site should be cleared, and so on.

# Schedules

A schedule is used to record repeated design information that applies to a range of components or fittings. Schedules are mainly used on bigger sites where there are multiples of several types of house (4-bedroom, 3-bedroom, 3-bedroom with dormers, etc.), each type having different components and fittings. The schedule avoids the wrong component or fitting being put in the wrong house. Schedules can also be used on smaller jobs such as a block of flats with 200 windows, where there are six different types of window.

The need for a specification depends on the complexity of the job and the number of repeated designs that there are. Schedules are mainly used to record repeated design information for:

- doors
- windows
- ironmongery
- joinery fitments
- sanitary components
- heating components and radiators
- kitchens.

A schedule is usually used in conjunction with a range drawing and a floor plan.

The following are basic examples of these documents, using a window as an example:

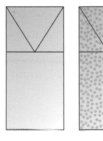   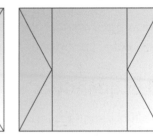

Window 1    Window 2    Window 3    Window 4    Window 5

**Figure 2.1** Range drawing

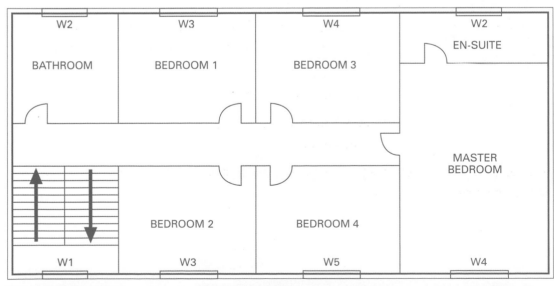

**Figure 2.2** Floor plan

## Activity

Schedules are not always needed on contracts, particularly smaller ones. Think of a job/contract that would require a schedule and produce one for a certain part of that job: for example, doors or brick types.

| WINDOW | SIZE | EXTERIOR | INTERIOR | LOCATION | GLASS | FIXING |
|---|---|---|---|---|---|---|
| Window 1 | 600 × 1200 mm | Mahogany wood grain UPVC | White UPVC | Stairwell | 22 mm thermal resistant double glazed units | Fixed with 100 mm frame fixing screws |
| Window 2 | 600 × 1200 mm | Mahogany wood grain UPVC | White UPVC | Bathroom En-suite | 22 mm thermal resistant double glazed units with maple leaf obscure pattern | Fixed with 100 mm frame fixing screws |
| Window 3 | 1100 × 1200 mm | Mahogany wood grain UPVC | White UPVC | Bedroom 1 Bedroom 2 | 22 mm thermal resistant double glazed units | Fixed with 100 mm frame fixing screws |
| Window 4 | 1100 × 1200 mm | Mahogany wood grain UPVC | White UPVC | Bedroom 3 Master bedroom | 22 mm thermal resistant double glazed units | Fixed with 100 mm frame fixing screws |
| Window 5 | 1500 × 1200 mm | Mahogany wood grain UPVC | White UPVC | Bedroom 4 | 22 mm thermal resistant double glazed units | Fixed with 100 mm frame fixing screws |

**Figure 2.3** Schedule for a window

The schedule shows that there are five types of window, each differing in size and appearance; the range drawing shows what each type of window looks like; and the floor plan shows which window goes where. For example, the bathroom window is a type two window, which is 1200 × 600 × 50 mm with a top-opening sash and obscure glass.

## Bill of quantities

The bill of quantities is produced by the quantity surveyor. It gives a complete description of everything that is required to do the job, including labour, materials and any items or components, drawing on information from the drawings, specification and schedule. The same single bill of quantities is sent out to all **prospective** contractors so they can submit a tender based on the same information – this helps the client select the best contractor for the job.

### Activity

Bills of quantities are used to help contractors provide a tender for a contract. Think of a simple task, then create a bill of quantities for that task, including labour, materials, and so on.

Every item needed should be listed on the bill of quantities

All bills of quantities contain the following information:

- **preliminaries** – general information such as the names of the client and architect, details of the work and descriptions of the site

- **preambles** – similar to the specification, outlining the quality and description of materials and workmanship, etc.

- **measured quantities** – a description of how each task or material is measured with measurements in metres (linear and square), hours, litres, kilograms or simply the number of components required

- **provisional quantities** – approximate amounts where items or components cannot be measured accurately

- **cost** – the amount of money that will be charged per unit of quantity.

The bill of quantities may also contain:

- any costs that may result from using sub-contractors or specialists

- a sum of money for work that has not been finally detailed

- a sum of money to cover contingencies for unforeseen work.

This is an extract from a bill of quantities that might be sent to prospective contractors, who would then complete the cost section and return it as their tender.

| Item ref No | Description | Quantity | Unit | Rate £ | Cost £ |
|---|---|---|---|---|---|
| A1 | Treated 50 × 225 mm sawn carcass | 200 | M | | |
| A2 | Treated 75 × 225 mm sawn carcass | 50 | M | | |
| B1 | 50 mm galvanised steel joist hangers | 20 | N/A | | |
| B2 | 75 mm galvanised steel joist hangers | 7 | N/A | | |
| C1 | Supply and fit the above floor joists as described in the preambles | | | | |

**Figure 2.4** Sample extract from a bill of quantities

To ensure that all contractors interpret and understand the bill of quantities consistently, the Royal Institution of Chartered Surveyors and the Building Employers' Confederation produce a document called the *Standard Method of Measurement of Building Works* (SMM). This provides a uniform basis for measuring building work, for example stating that carcassing timber is measured by the metre whereas plasterboard is measured in square metres.

## Conditions of contract

Almost all building work is carried out under a contract. A small job with a single client (e.g. a loft conversion) will have a basic contract stating that the contractor will do the work to the client's satisfaction, and that the client will pay the contractor the agreed sum of money once the work is finished.

Larger contracts with clients such as the Government will have additional clauses, terms or **stipulations** written into the contract. Most large contracts are awarded to companies not solely on the basis of cost, but also taking into account the benefits of the package offered for both the community and the environment.

Clauses, terms or stipulations may include any of the following.

### Environmental management

At the tendering stage of a project, most government bodies or large, privately run companies will ask potential contractors to specify how they will manage waste and recycling, and how they will minimise the impact on the environment (for example, by re-planting uprooted trees or moving plants and vegetation instead of destroying them).

Companies will be monitored against their own targets and, if they fail to meet them, may face a financial penalty. Because of this, tendering companies may underestimate their targets for a tender: for example, by stating that they will use 15 per cent recycled/re-used materials on the project rather than 20 per cent.

### Health and safety management

On particularly large contracts, tendering companies will provide written safety policy and mission statements, stating how they will do the job safely.

### Local workforce/suppliers/materials management

A good tender will specify the proportion of local workers that will be used during the work, in an effort to help bolster the local economy and reduce local unemployment. Using local suppliers or materials that are produced locally is also considered good practice for successful tenders.

### Community regeneration management

Some companies will commit to upgrading or improving communities as part of their tender. For example, a company tendering to build a block of flats may commit to building play parks, youth clubs or other community amenities.

After the tender has been agreed, further conditions may be added to the contract, as follows.

## Variations

A variation is a modification of the original drawing or specification. The architect or client must give the contractor written confirmation of the variation, then the contractor submits a price for the variation to the quantity surveyor (or client, on a small job). Once the price is accepted, the variation work can be completed.

## Interim payment

An **interim** payment schedule may be written into the contract, meaning that the client pays for the work in instalments. The client may pay an amount each month, linked to how far the job has progressed, or may make regular payments regardless of how far the job has progressed.

## Final payment

Here the client makes a one-off full payment once the job has been completed to the specification. A final payment scheme may also have additional clauses included, such as:

- **retention**
  This is when the client holds a small percentage of the full payment back for a specified period (usually six months).  It may take some time for any defects to show, such as cracks in plaster. If the contractor fixes the defects, they will receive the retention payment; if they don't fix them, the retention payment can be used to hire another contractor to do so.

- **penalty clause**
  This is usually introduced in contracts with a tight deadline, where the building must be finished and ready to operate on time. If the project overruns, the client will be unable to trade in the premises and will lose money, so the contractor will have to compensate the client for lost revenue.

### Did you know?

On a poorly run contract, a penalty clause can be very costly and could incur a substantial payment. In an extreme case, the contractor may end up making a loss instead of a profit on the project.

It is vital you check the exact terms of each contract

## Knowledge refresher

1 Name four people who are involved in creating contract documents.

2 What is the purpose of a specification?

3 List four things that should be contained in a specification.

4 What is the purpose of a schedule?

5 Who produces the bill of quantities and what is its main purpose?

6 State why companies will add stipulations to their tender.

7 Describe what a variation is in regards to contract conditions.

8 Describe a penalty clause.

## What would you do?

You have been invited to tender a bid for a large public contract. Business has been slow, and you really need it if you are to keep your business afloat and avoid redundancies.

Two of the other tenders concern you. One is priced so low that, if you match it, you may make a small loss. In the other, the contractor promises to recycle 45% of materials, to use only sustainable materials and to employ 70% of the local workforce – matching this may mean you have to lay off some workers and may only make a small profit.

What should you do? What stipulations could you introduce to help improve your bid? What could the consequences be of not getting the contract – or, indeed, of getting it?

# The Building Regulations

The Building Regulations were first introduced in the late 19th century to improve the appalling housing conditions common then. The Public Health Act 1875 allowed local authorities to make their own laws regarding the planning and construction of buildings. There were many grey areas and **inconsistencies** between local authorities, especially where one authority bordered another.

This system remained in place for almost a century until the Building Regulations 1965 came into force. These replaced all local laws with a uniform Act for all in England and Wales to follow. The only exception was inner London, which was covered by the London Building Acts. The Government passed a new law in 1984, setting up the Building Regulations 1985 to cover all England and Wales, including inner London.

The current law is the Building Regulations 2000, amended in April 2006 to take into account things such as wheelchair access and more environmentally friendly practices. The current law also covers all England and Wales.

Building Regulations help protect the environment

**Find out**

For more about the Building Regulations, visit www.ukbuildingstandards.org.uk

**Remember**

Building regulations can change over time. Always be sure you are using the most updated version.

Scotland is governed slightly differently and is covered by the Building (Scotland) Act 2003. Northern Ireland is covered by the Building (Amendment) Regulations (Northern Ireland) 2006 which came into effect on November 2006.

The main purpose of the Building Regulations is to ensure the health, safety and welfare of all people in and around buildings as well as to further energy conservation and to protect the environment. The regulations apply to most new buildings as well as any alterations to existing buildings, whether they are domestic, commercial or industrial.  Many projects also require planning permission, which will be covered in Chapter 3.

The regulations are broken down into several categories:

- Part A – Structural safety
- Part B – Fire safety
- Part C – Resistance to moisture and weather
- Part D – Toxic substances
- Part E – Resistance to sound
- Part F – Ventilation
- Part G – Hygiene
- Part H – Drainage and waste disposal
- Part J – Heat-producing appliances
- Part K – Protection from falling
- Part L – Conservation of fuel and power
- Part M – Access to and use of buildings
- Part N – Glazing safety
- Part P – Electrical safety.

Each of these sections contains an 'approved document', detailing what is covered by that part of the regulations:

**Approved document A**

A1 – Loading

A2 – Ground movement

A3 – Disproportionate collapse

**Approved document B**

B1 – Means of warning and escape

B2 – Internal fire spread (linings)

B3 – Internal fire spread (structure)

B4 – External fire spread

B5 – Access and facilities for the fire service

**Approved document C**

C1 – Site preparation and resistance to contaminates

C2 – Resistance to moisture

**Approved document D**

D1 – Cavity insulation

**Approved document E**

E1 – Protection against sound from other parts of the building and adjoining buildings

E2 – Protection against sound within a dwelling-house, etc.

E3 – Reverberation in the common internal parts of buildings containing flats or rooms for residential purposes

E4 – Acoustic conditions in schools

**Approved document F** deals only with ventilation

## Approved document G

G1 – Sanitary conveniences and washing facilities

G2 – Bathrooms

G3 – Hot water storage

## Approved document H

H1 – Foul water drainage

H2 – Wastewater treatment systems and cesspools

H3 – Rainwater drainage

H4 – Building over sewers

H5 – Separate systems of drainage

H6 – Solid waste storage

## Approved document J

J1 – Air supply

J2 – Discharge of products of combustion

J3 – Protection of building

J4 – Provision of information

J5 – Protection of liquid fuel storage systems

J6 – Protection against pollution

## Approved document K

K1 – Stairs, ladders and ramps

K2 – Protection from falling

K3 – Vehicle barriers and loading bays

K4 – Protection from collision with open windows, skylights and ventilators

K5 – Protection against impact from and trapping by doors

## Approved document L

L1A – Conservation of fuel and power in new dwellings

L1B – Conservation of fuel and power in existing dwellings

L2A – Conservation of fuel and power in new buildings other than dwellings

L2B – Conservation of fuel and power in existing buildings other than dwellings

## Approved document M

M1 – Access and use

M2 – Access to extensions to buildings other than dwellings

M3 – Sanitary conveniences in extensions to buildings other than dwellings

M4 – Sanitary conveniences in dwellings

## Approved document N

N1 – Protection against impact

N2 – Manifestation of glazing

N3 – Safe opening and closing of windows, skylights and ventilators

N4 – Safe access for cleaning windows, etc.

## Approved document P

P1 – Design and installation of electrical installations

## Activity

The Building Inspector's role is vital in enforcing the Building Regulations. Think of a medium-sized job that you are familiar with. What do you think a Building Inspector would need to check on that job?

These are the types of work classified as needing Building Regulations approval:

- the erection of an extension or building

- the installation or extension of a service or fitting which is controlled under the regulations

- an alteration project involving work which will temporarily or permanently affect the ongoing compliance of the building, service, or fitting with the requirements relating to structure, fire, or access to and the use of the building

- the insertion of insulation into a cavity wall

- the underpinning of the foundations of a building

- work affecting the thermal elements, energy status or energy performance of the building.

If you are unsure whether the work you are going to carry out needs Building Regulations approval, contact the local authority.

The Building Regulations are enforced by two types of building control bodies: local authority building control and Approved Inspector building control. If you wish to apply for approval, you must contact one of these bodies.

If you use an Approved Inspector, you must contact the local authority to tell them what is being done where, stating that the Inspector will be responsible for the control of the work.

If you choose to go to the local authority, there are three ways of applying for consent:

- **Full plans** – Plans are submitted to the local authority along with any specifications and other contract documents. The local authority scrutinises these and makes a decision.

- **Building notice** – A less detailed amount of information is submitted (but more can be requested) and no decision is made. The approval process is determined by the stage the work is at.

- **Regularisation** – This is a means of applying for approval for work that has already been completed without approval.

The Building Inspector will make regular visits to ensure that the work is being carried out to the standards set down in the application, and that no extra unapproved work is being done. Often the contractor will tell the Inspector when the job has reached a certain stage, so that they can come in and check what has been done. If the Inspector is not informed at key stages, he/she can ask for the work to be opened up to be checked.

Building Regulations approval is not always given but there is an appeals procedure. For more information, contact your local authority.

## Activity

Think of a job you have done or seen that has been carried out poorly. What improvements might a Building Inspector request?

The Building Inspector will need to be involved at every key stage

# Knowledge refresher

1  What is the main purpose of the Building Regulations?

2  Which approved document deals with stairs?

3  Which approved document deals with conservation of fuel and power?

4  What does approved document F deal with?

5  List four types of work that would require Building Regulations approval.

6  Who can you contact to check if the work you are doing requires Building Regulations approval?

7  What is the role of the Building Inspector?

## What would you do?

You are part way through building an extension when the client asks for an alteration to the original plans. You think that this alteration may need Building Regulations approval, but applying now would put the job back a few weeks, and you are already under time pressure. The client says they do not care about the Building Regulations; they want the work done now, or they will stop paying you. What should you do? What could the repercussions of your actions be?

# General site paperwork

No building site could function properly without a certain amount of paperwork. Here is a brief, but not exhaustive, description of some of the other documents you may encounter. Some companies will have their own forms to cover such things as scaffolding checks.

## Timesheet

Timesheets record hours worked, and are completed by every employee individually. Some timesheets are basic, asking just for a brief description of the work done each hour, but some can be complicated. In some cases timesheets may be used to work out how many hours the client will be charged for.

## P. Gresford Building Contractors

**Timesheet** _____

**Employee** _____     **Project/site** _____

| Date | Job no. | Start time | Finish time | Total time | Travel time | Expenses |
|------|---------|-----------|-------------|-----------|-------------|----------|
| M    |         |           |             |           |             |          |
| Tu   |         |           |             |           |             |          |
| W    |         |           |             |           |             |          |
| Th   |         |           |             |           |             |          |
| F    |         |           |             |           |             |          |
| Sa   |         |           |             |           |             |          |
| Su   |         |           |             |           |             |          |
| Totals |       |           |             |           |             |          |

**Employee's signature** _____

**Supervisor's signature** _____

**Date** _____

**Figure 2.5** Timesheet

## Day worksheets

Day worksheets are often confused with timesheets, but are different as they are used when there is no price or estimate for the work, to enable the contractor to charge for the work. Day worksheets record work done, hours worked and sometimes materials used. They are also used when variation orders or extra work is added to a contract.

### P. Gresford Building Contractors

**Day worksheet** _____

Customer _Chris MacFarlane_____     Date _____

Description of work being carried out _____
_Hang internal door in kitchen._
_____

| Labour | Craft | Hours | Gross rate | TOTALS |
|--------|-------|-------|------------|--------|
|  |  |  |  |  |
|  |  |  |  |  |
| Materials | Quantity | Rate | % addition |  |
|  |  |  |  |  |
|  |  |  |  |  |
| Plant | Hours | Rate | % addition |  |
|  |  |  |  |  |
|  |  |  |  |  |

| Comments |
|----------|
|  |

Signed _____     Date _____

Site manager/foreman signature _____

**Figure 2.6** Day worksheet

### P. Gresford Building Contractors

**Job sheet** _____

Customer   Chris MacFarlane
_____

Address   1 High Street
          Any Town
          Any County
_____

**Work to be carried out**
Hang internal door in kitchen
_____

**Special conditions/instructions**
Fit with door closer
3 × 75 mm butt hinges

**Figure 2.7** Job sheet

## Job sheet

A job sheet is similar to a day worksheet – it records work done – but is used when the work has already been priced. Job sheets enable the worker to see what needs to be done and the site agent or working foreman to see what has been completed.

## Variation order

This sheet is used by the architect to make any changes to the original plans, including omissions, alterations and extra work.

**VARIATION TO PROPOSED WORKS AT 123 A STREET**

REFERENCE NO:

DATE _____

FROM _____

TO _____

POSSIBLE VARIATIONS TO WORK AT 123 A STREET

| ADDITIONS |
| --- |
|  |
|  |
|  |
|  |

| OMISSIONS |
| --- |
|  |
|  |
|  |
|  |

SIGNED -----------------------------------------

**Figure 2.8** Variation order

## Confirmation notice

This is a sheet given to the contractor to confirm any changes made in the variation order, so that the contractor can go ahead and carry out the work.

**CONFIRMATION FOR VARIATION TO PROPOSED WORKS AT 123 A STREET**

REFERENCE NO:

DATE _____

FROM _____

TO _____

I CONFIRM THAT I HAVE RECEIVED WRITTEN INSTRUCTIONS
FROM _____
POSITION _____
TO CARRY OUT THE FOLLOWING POSSIBLE VARIATIONS TO THE ABOVE NAMED CONTRACT

| ADDITIONS |
| --- |
|  |
|  |

| OMISSIONS |
| --- |
|  |
|  |
|  |

SIGNED -----------------------------------------

**Figure 2.9** Confirmation notice

## Orders/requisitions

A requisition form or order is used to order materials or components from a supplier.

## P. Gresford Building Contractors

**Requisition form**

Supplier _____     Order no. _____
_____     Serial no. _____

Tel no. _____     Contact _____

Fax no. _____     Our ref _____

Contract/Delivery address/Invoice address     Statements/applications
_____     for payments to be sent to
_____     _____
Tel no. _____     _____
Fax no. _____     _____

| Item no. | Quantity | Unit | Description | Unit price | Amount |
|---|---|---|---|---|---|
|  |  |  |  |  |  |
|  |  |  |  |  |  |
|  |  |  |  |  |  |
|  |  |  |  |  |  |

Total £ _____

Payment terms _____     Date _____

Originated by _____

Authorised by _____

**Figure 2.10** Requisition form

## Delivery notes

Delivery notes are given to the contractor by the supplier, and list all the materials and components being delivered. Each delivery note should be checked for accuracy against the order (to ensure what is being delivered is what was asked for) and against the delivery itself (to make sure that the delivery matches the delivery note). If there are any **discrepancies** or if the delivery is of a poor quality or damaged, you must write on the delivery note what is wrong before signing it and ensure the site agent is informed so that he/she can rectify the problem.

## Bailey & Sons Ltd

*Building materials supplier*

Tel: 01234 567890

**Your ref:** AB00671

**Our ref:** CT020

**Order no:** 67440387

**Date:** 17 Jul 2006

**Invoice address:**
Carillion Training Centre,
Deptford Terrace, Sunderland

**Delivery address:**
Same as invoice

| Description of goods | Quantity | Catalogue no. |
|---|---|---|
| OPC 25kg | 10 | OPC1.1 |
|  |  |  |

Comments:

Date and time of receiving goods:

Name of recipient (caps):

Signature:

**Figure 2.11** Delivery note

INVOICE

**JARVIS BUILDING SUPPLIES**
*3RD AVENUE*
*THOMASTOWN*

L Weeks Builders
4th Grove
Thomastown

| Quantity | Description | Unit price | Vat rate | Total |
|---|---|---|---|---|
| 30 | Galvanised joint hangers | £1.32 | 17.5% | £46.53 |
|  |  |  |  |  |
|  |  |  |  |  |
|  |  |  |  |  |
|  |  |  |  |  |
|  |  |  |  |  |
|  |  |  |  |  |
|  |  |  |  | TOTAL | £46.53 |

To be paid within 30 days from receipt of this invoice

Please direct any queries to 01234 56789

**Figure 2.12** Invoice

## Invoices

Invoices come from a variety of sources such as suppliers or sub-contractors, and state what has been provided and how much the contractor will be charged for it.

### Remember

Invoices may need paying by a certain date – fines for late payment can sometimes be incurred – so it is important that they are passed on to the finance office or financial controller promptly.

**JARVIS BUILDING SUPPLIES**
*3rd AVENUE*
*THOMASTOWN*

Customer ref_____

Customer order date_____

Delivery date_____

| Item no | Qty Supplied | Qty to follow | Description | Unit price |
|---------|--------------|---------------|-------------|------------|
| 1 | 30 | 0 | Galvanised joinst hangers | £1.32 |
| | | | | |
| | | | | |
| | | | | |
| | | | | |

Delivered to: L Weeks builders
4th Grove
Thomastown
Customer signature _ _ _ _ _ _ _ _ _ _ _ _ _ _ _ _ _ _ _ _ _

## Delivery records

Delivery records list all deliveries over a certain period (usually a month), and are sent to the contractor's Head Office so that payment can be made.

**Figure 2.13** Delivery record

## Remember

Remember – you should always check a delivery note against the order and the delivery itself, then write any discrepancies or problems on the delivery note *before* signing it.

## Daily report/site diary

This is used to pass general information (deliveries, attendance, etc.) on to a company's Head Office.

**Figure 2.14** Daily report or site diary

**DAILY REPORT/SITE DIARY**

PROJECT_____
DATE_____

Identify any of the following factors, which are affecting or may affect the daily work activities and give a brief description in the box provided

WEATHER ( )  ACCESS ( )  ACCIDENTS ( )  SERVICES ( )
DELIVERIES ( )  SUPPLIES ( )  LABOUR ( )  OTHER ( )

SIGNED _ _ _ _ _ _ _ _ _ _ _ _ _ _ _ _ _ _ _ _ _ _ _ _ _ _ _
POSITION _ _ _ _ _ _ _ _ _ _ _ _ _ _ _ _ _ _ _ _ _ _ _ _ _ _

## Accident and near miss reports

It is a legal requirement that a company has an accident book, in which reports of all accidents must be made. Reports must also be made when an accident nearly happened, but did not in the end occur – known as a 'near miss'. It is everyone's responsibility to complete the accident book. If you are also in a supervisory position you will have the responsibility to ensure all requirements for accident reporting are met.

### Safety tip

If you are involved in or witness an accident or near miss, make sure it is entered in the book – for your own safety and that of others on the site. If you don't report it, it's more likely to happen again.

### Report of an Accident, Dangerous Occurrence or Near Miss

**Date of incident** ____________ **Time of incident** ____________

**Location of incident** ____________

**Details of person involved in accident**

Name ____________ Date of birth ____________

Address ____________

____________

____________ Occupation ____________

**Date off work (if applicable)** ____________ **Date returning to work** ____________

**Nature of injury** ____________

**Management of injury** ☐ First Aid only ☐ Advised to see doctor ☐ Sent to casualty ☐ Admitted to hospital

**Account of accident, dangerous occurrence or near miss**
(Continued on separate sheet if necessary)

**Witnesses to the incident**
(Names, addresses and occupations)

**Was the injured person wearing PPE? If yes, what PPE?** ____________

____________

**Signature of person completing form** ____________

**Occupation** ____________ **Date** ____________

**Figure 2.15** Accident/near miss report

## Method statement

Sometimes known as a 'safe system of work', a method statement details the way a task or process will be carried out safely. It includes a step-by-step guide, outlines the hazards involved, and describes the control measures that have been introduced to ensure the safety of anyone affected. Written method statements are often requested at the tender stage, so that the client can be sure of the company's safety credentials.

### Activity

Think of a simple task you are familiar with and write a method statement for that task.

## FAQ

### How do I know what scale the drawing is at?

The scale should be written on the title panel (the box included on a plan or drawing giving basic information such as who drew it, how to contact them, the date and the scale).

### How do I know if I need a schedule?

Schedules are only really used in large jobs where there is a lot of repeated design information. If your job has a lot of doors, windows, etc., it is a good idea to use one.

### How do I know if I need approval?

If you are unsure, check section three of the Building Regulations or contact your local authority.

### Do I need to know all the different Building Regulations and what is contained in each section?

No, but a good understanding of what is involved is needed.

### How many different forms are there?

A lot of forms are used and some companies use more than others. You should ensure you get the relevant training on completing the form before using it.

# Knowledge refresher

1   What is the difference between a timesheet and day worksheet?

2   What is a variation order?

3   What is a daily site diary used for?

4   Why are near miss reports used?

5   What is a method statement?

# What would you do?

1   You are working on a renovation project when your boss calls you to ask what materials you need for the next few weeks. You are caught a bit off-guard, and you rush around giving your boss a list of materials over the phone. When the materials are delivered, there are some discrepancies: it's not what you said, as far as you can remember. You phone your boss to tell him and he gets cross, blaming you for the mistakes. Who is to blame? What should have been done?

2   A friend has approached you to do a loft conversion. You apply for planning permission and Building Regulations approval and are given both, so you start work. You come across a problem with the chimney and decide to remove some of the bricks. With the work completed, the Building Inspector shows up to check the job. What can the Building Inspector do? What effect could this have on the job? What could have been done to prevent it?

# Planning and work programmes

## OVERVIEW

Any building project begins long before the first brick is laid or the first foundation dug. Most buildings and construction projects will need some sort of planning approval before they get underway, as a range of planning restrictions are in place to keep building standards up, protect local people and protect the environment.

Work planning is also of paramount importance for every job, whether a single dwelling or a large housing estate. Without it even the smallest job can go wrong: something simple is forgotten or omitted, such as ordering a skip, and the job is suddenly delayed by anything up to a week. On a smaller job, poor planning can result in delays, which will harm your reputation and jeopardise future contracts. With larger contracts, penalty clauses can be costly: if the job overruns and isn't finished on time, the client may claim substantial amounts of money from the contractor.

This chapter will deal with:

- planning permission
- work programming.

# Planning permission

Before starting to plan a building project, it is important to know how your plans may be affected by local and national building restrictions. The two main sets of restrictions you will come across are:

- the Building Regulations
- planning permission.

We looked at the Building Regulations in Chapter 2, so here we will look at planning permission. It is crucial that anyone planning a construction project understands how this works, and seeks the necessary approval in the correct way. If not, building work runs the risk of having to be halted, altered or even taken down.

Planning permission laws were introduced to stop people building whatever they like wherever they like. The submission of a planning application gives both the local authority and the general public a chance to look at the development, to see if it is in keeping with the local area and whether it serves the interests of the local community.

The main **remit** of planning laws is to control the use and development of land in order to obtain the greatest possible environmental advantages with the least inconvenience for both the person/s applying for permission and society as a whole.

The key word in planning is 'development', defined in planning law as 'the carrying out of building, engineering, mining or other operations in, on, over or under land, or the making of any material change in the use of any buildings or other land'. As well as building work, this covers the construction of a new road or driveway, and even change of use: if a bank is to be turned into a wine bar, planning permission will be needed.

Planning permission is required for most forms of development. Here are a few more examples of work requiring planning permission:

- virtually all new building work
- house extensions including conservatories, loft conversions and roof additions (such as dormers)
- buildings and other structures on the land including garages
- adding a porch to your house
- putting up a TV satellite dish.

Even if you are intending to work from home and wish to convert part of your home into an office, you will require planning permission if:

- your home is no longer to be used mainly as a private residence
- your business creates more traffic or creates problems with parking due to people calling

## Definition

**Remit** – scope, job, the areas an organisation or individual has to cover

## Did you know?

Planning permission is needed if you want to put up a satellite dish. The job itself is small and not disruptive, but a dish is thought to change the outer appearance of a house enough to need permission.

- your business involves any activities classed as unusual in a **residential** area
- your business disturbs your neighbours at unreasonable hours or creates other forms of nuisance or smell.

Not all work requires planning. You can make certain types of minor alterations to your house, such as putting up a fence or dividing wall (providing it is less than 1 metre high next to a highway, or under 2 metres elsewhere), without planning permission.

In areas such as conservation areas or classified Areas of Outstanding Natural Beauty there will be stricter controls on what is allowed. Listed buildings also have stricter controls and come under the Planning (Listed Buildings and Conservation Areas) Act 1990.

For planning permission, you must apply to your local council. When they look at your proposed works, they will take into consideration:

- the number, size, positioning, layout and external appearance of the buildings
- the proposed means of access, landscaping and impact on the neighbourhood
- **sustainability**, and whether the necessary infrastructure, such as roads, services, etc., will be available
- the proposed use of the development.

Several steps are involved in applying for planning permission. The first is to contact the local authority to see if they think planning permission is required (some councils may charge a small fee for this advice). If they say you do need planning permission, you need to then ask them for an application form. There are two types of planning permission that you can apply for:

- **Outline application** This can be made if you want to see what the council thinks of the building work you intend to do before you go to the trouble of having costly plans drawn up. Details of the work will have to be submitted later if the outline application is successful.

> **Definition**
>
> **Residential** – where people live, rather than a business district, for example

> **Definition**
>
> **Sustainability**– the ability to last or carry on, how easy something is to keep going

The public has a right to know about proposed developments

- **Full application** Here a full application is made with all the plans, specifications, and so on.

Once you have completed the relevant form this must be sent to the local authority along with any fee.

Next, the contents of your application will be publicised so that people can express their views and raise any objections. A copy will be placed in the planning register; an electronic version will be placed on the local authority's website; and immediate neighbours will be written to (or a fixed notice will be displayed on or as near as possible to the site). The local authority may also advertise your application in a local newspaper. As the applicant, you will be entitled to have a copy of any reports, objections and expressions of support the local authority receives regarding your application.

The local authority normally takes up to eight weeks to make a decision on your application but in some cases it may take longer. If this happens, the local authority should write asking for your written consent to extend the period. If your application is not dealt with within eight weeks, you can appeal to the Secretary of State, but this can be a lengthy procedure itself, so it is best to try to resolve the matter at a local level.

In looking at an application, the local authority considers whether there are valid reasons for refusing or granting permission: the local authority cannot simply reject a proposal because many people oppose it. The local authority will look at whether your proposal is consistent with the area's appearance, whether it will cause traffic problems and whether it has any impact on local amenities, environment and services.

Once an application has been looked at, there are four possible outcomes: permission refused; application still pending; granted with conditions; or granted.

- **Permission refused**

  If permission is refused, the local authority must state its reasons for turning down the application. If you feel these are unfair, you can appeal to the Secretary of State. Appeals must be made within six months of the local authority's decision and are intended as a last resort. It can take months to get a decision, which may be a refusal. Alternatively, you can ask what changes need to be made to allow the proposal to pass: if these are acceptable, the amended application can be submitted for processing. If after this the application is still rejected, the work cannot go ahead. However, different authorities have different procedures, so always check before submitting proposals.

- **Application still pending**

  Here the local authority may have found that it needs extra time to allow comments to come in, or to deal with particular issues that have arisen. If the application is still pending then, as stated previously, the local authority must ask for your written consent to extend the period for making a decision.

- **Granted with conditions**

  In this case you are able to start the work, remembering to comply with the conditions stated. If you fail to comply, permission will be revoked and you may be ordered to undo the work done. If you are unhappy with the conditions set, you can ask for advice and, if needs be, make alterations to the plans. This would mean resubmitting the application.

- **Granted**

  If you have been granted permission, you are free to start the work.

## Knowledge refresher

1   Why were planning permission laws introduced?

2   What is the main remit of planning laws?

3   Give five examples of work that would require planning permission.

4   Give one example of work that would not require planning permission.

5   Give a brief outline of the two types of planning permission you could apply for.

6   List the four possible outcomes of a planning application.

## What would you do?

You are working on a small job converting an attached garage into an extra bedroom. You have applied for planning permission and the application is still pending. The local authority say it should be fine, but there is one thing they need to check and it could take a few more weeks. This causes a problem for both you and the client: the client wants the work started and you have no other work to do for a few weeks. What do you do? What could the repercussions be? What could you do to protect yourself?

# Work programming

Once planning permission and Building Regulations approval have been obtained, the next step is to plan the work (NB in some instances the client may ask the contractor to provide a work programme at the tender stage, to check the contractor's efficiency and organising ability).

A work programme is vital for good work planning, as it shows:

- what tasks are to be done and when, including any overlap in the tasks
- what materials are required and when
- what plant is needed, when and for how long
- what type of workforce is required and when.

A few different types of work programme are in use, and we will cover the main two here.

## Planning the site

For every fair-sized job, the building site needs to be carefully planned. A poorly planned site can cause problems and delays, as well as incurring costs and even causing accidents.

A building site should be seen as a temporary workshop, store and office for the contractor, and must contain all the **amenities** needed on a permanent base. Sites should be planned in a way that minimises the movement of employees, materials and plant throughout the construction, while at the same time providing protection and security for employees, materials and components, and members of the public. A well-planned site will also have good transport routes, which will not disrupt the site or the general traffic.

Many things need to be included on a building site, so it is often easiest to plan your site using a site plan and cut-outs of the amenities you need. These cut-outs can be laid onto the plan and moved around until a suitable layout is found.

The ideal layout of the site will vary according to the size and **duration** of the job – there is no point hiring site offices for a job that will only last a day! The following gives an idea of what might be needed on an average site:

- **Site offices**

    The office space (usually portable cabins) should be of a decent size, usually with more than one room for different members of staff and a large room for meetings. Phone, fax and email facilities will be needed, so that the site office can communicate with Head Office, contractors, suppliers and others. As with any office, the site office must be heated, have plenty of light (natural or artificial) and be fitted out with useful, comfortable furniture.

## Remember

If you need to plan several sites, save the cut-outs from one to use on the next (checking that you are using the same scale). You could end up with a 'kit' to use whenever you need it.

## Definition

**Amenities** – facilities such as toilets, rest areas, etc.

**Duration** – how long something goes on

- **First aid office**

  This is sometimes contained within the site office, but on larger sites a separate space may be needed so that injured people can be treated quickly and efficiently. The first aid office must be fully stocked, and there must be sufficient trained first aiders on site.

- **Toilets**

  There must be sufficient toilets on the site. Usually there will be a WC block next to the canteen or mess area, with additional portable toilets dotted around the site if needed. Toilets must be kept clean and well stocked at all times, and have somewhere for people to wash their hands. The WC block may also need to house showers if the work being done requires them.

- **Lunch area**

  This should be protected from the wind and rain and have heating and electricity. It should contain equipment such as a microwave, kettle or urn and fridge to heat and keep food, as well as suitable food storage such as cupboards. There should be adequate seating and tables, and the space should be kept clean to prevent any unwelcome pests such as rats or cockroaches.

- **Drying room**

  This provides space for employees to dry off any clothes that get wet, on the way to or during work. It is usually sited next to the lunch area, or is part of the same building. The room must have adequate heating and ventilation, as well as lockers or storage to house things like motorcycle helmets.

- **Cranes, hoists, etc.**

  These can be static or portable. When a large static crane is required, its position needs to be planned so that it can easily and safely reach the area where it is needed. Larger cranes should be situated away from the main site office for safety reasons.

- **Transport route**

  Having a good transport route into, out of and within a building site is vital. It is best to have separate entrances and exits, with a one-way system on the site and good signposting throughout. These measures will avoid large delivery lorries having to turn around on site, and help to keep both internal and external traffic flowing with minimum disruption.

- **Waste area**

  This must be well away from the lunch area for health and safety reasons, and should be easily accessible from the transport route so that the skips and bins can be emptied easily. Separate well-labelled skips are needed for different kinds of refuse, and there should be some for recycling. Certain skips should be kept separate to avoid **contamination**, and chemical dumps (for paint, etc.) should be kept secure and emptied regularly.

Various types of storage are also needed on a building site, such as:

- **materials storage** – enough adequate space to store all types of materials, ideally near to where they are being used (for example, cement and sand should be stored near the mixer). All materials should be stored in a way that prevents them being damaged or stolen; some materials will have to be stored separately to avoid contamination.

- **component storage** – a secure compound protected from the wind and rain for items such as doors and windows. Again, components should be stored in a way that prevents them being damaged.

- **tool storage** – a secure place for employees' own tools as well as site tools such as table saws. The tool storage area needs to be thoroughly secure to prevent theft.

- **ironmongery storage** – a locked compound in a container with well-labelled racks to avoid things like screws and nails being mixed up. Expensive ironmongery such as door furniture needs to be properly secure. On a well-planned site, expensive ironmongery is only ordered when needed.

A good site layout might look something like this.

## Activity

Design a site layout for a large project, placing all the amenities that you think may be required in an appropriate place.

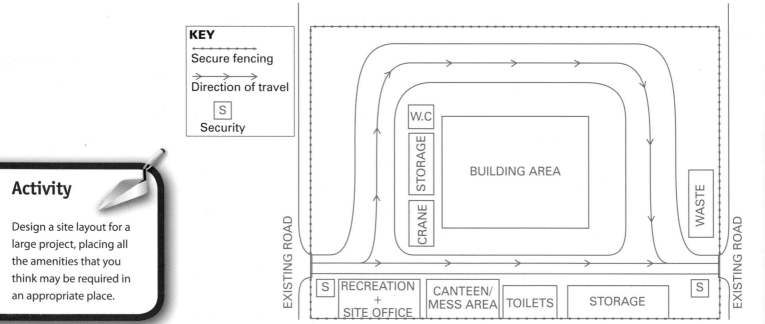

**Figure 3.1** Good site layout

## Planning the work

There are many types of work programme, including the critical path and the Bar/Gantt chart. The latter is the one you will come across most often.

## Bar charts

The bar or Gantt chart is the most popular work programme as it is simple to construct and easy to understand. Bar charts have tasks listed in a vertical column on the left and a horizontal timescale running along the top.

| Time in days | | | | | | | | | | |
|---|---|---|---|---|---|---|---|---|---|---|
| **Activity** | 1 | 2 | 3 | 4 | 5 | 6 | 7 | 8 | 9 | 10 |
| Dig for foundation and service routes | | | | | | | | | | |
| Lay foundations | | | | | | | | | | |
| Run cabling, piping, etc. to meet existing services | | | | | | | | | | |
| Build up to DPC | | | | | | | | | | |
| Lay concrete floor | | | | | | | | | | |

**Figure 3.2** Basic bar chart

Each task is given a proposed time, which is shaded in along the horizontal timescale. Timescales often overlap as one task often overlaps another.

| Time in days | | | | | | | | | | |
|---|---|---|---|---|---|---|---|---|---|---|
| **Activity** | 1 | 2 | 3 | 4 | 5 | 6 | 7 | 8 | 9 | 10 |
| Dig for foundation and service routes | ■ | ■ | | | | | | | | |
| Lay foundations | | | ■ | ■ | | | | | | |
| Run cabling, piping, etc. to meet existing services | | | | ■ | ■ | | | | | |
| Build up to DPC | | | | | | ■ | ■ | | | |
| Lay concrete floor | | | | | | | | ■ | ■ | ■ |

Key: proposed ■

**Figure 3.3** Bar chart showing proposed time for a contract

The bar chart can then be used to check progress. Often the actual time taken for a task is shaded in underneath the proposed time (in a different way or colour to avoid confusion). This shows how what *has* been done matches up to what *should have* been done.

**Did you know?**

The Gantt chart is named after the first man to publish it. This was Henry Gantt, an American engineer, in 1910.

**Activity**

Think of a task and create a bar chart for that task.

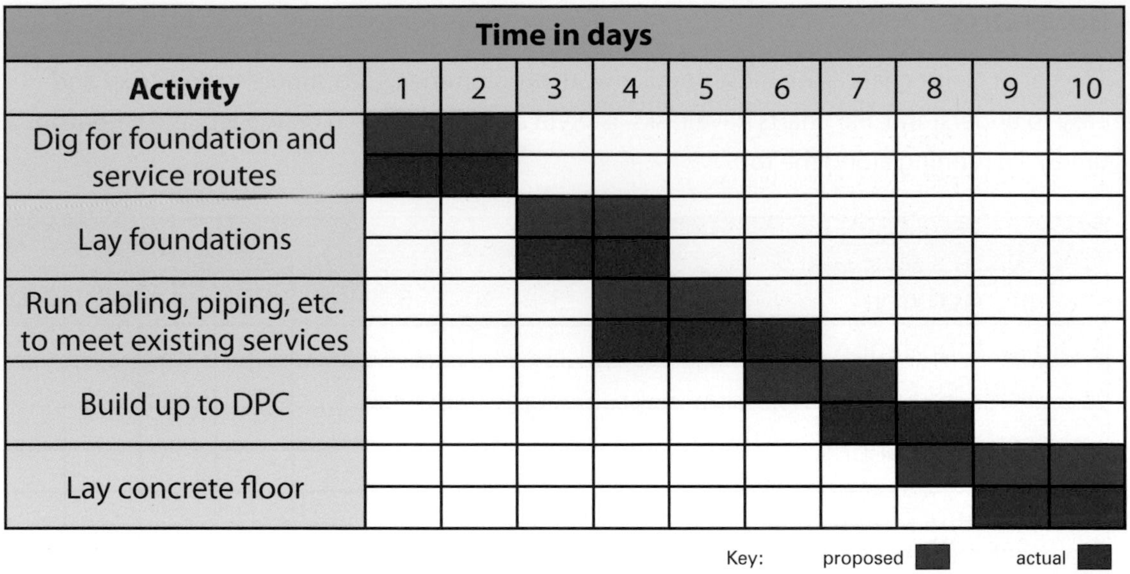
Time in days
Activity
1
2
3
4
5
6
7
8
9
10
Dig for foundation and service routes
Lay foundations
Run cabling, piping, etc. to meet existing services
Build up to DPC
Lay concrete floor
Key:
proposed
actual

**Figure 3.4** Bar chart showing actual time half way through a contract

## Activity

Using the bar chart you've created, think of what could go wrong and write a list of contingencies to overcome any problems.

As you can see, a bar chart can help you plan when to order materials or plant, see what trade is due in and when, and so on. A bar chart can also tell you if you are behind on a job; if you have a penalty clause written into your contract, this information is vital.

When creating a bar chart, you should build in some extra time to allow for things such as bad weather, labour shortages, delivery problems or illness. It is also advisable to have contingency plans to help solve or avoid problems, such as:

- capacity to work overtime to catch up time
- bonus scheme to increase productivity
- penalty clause on suppliers to try to avoid late or poor deliveries
- source of extra labour (e.g. from another site) if needed.

Good planning, with contingency plans in place, should allow a job to run smoothly and finish on time, leading to the contractor making a profit.

## Did you know?

Bad weather is the main external factor responsible for delays on building sites in the UK. A Met Office survey showed that the average UK construction company experiences problems caused by the weather 26 times a year.

## *Critical paths*

Another form of work programme is the critical path. Critical paths are rarely used these days as they can be difficult to decipher. The final part of this chapter will give a brief overview of the basics of a critical path, in case you should come across one.

A critical path can be used in the same way as a bar chart to show what needs to be done and in what sequence. It also shows a timescale but in a different way to a bar chart: each timescale shows both the minimum and the maximum amount of time a task might take.

The critical path is shown as a series of circles called event nodes. Each node is split into three: the top third shows the event number, the bottom left shows the earliest start time, and the bottom right the latest start time.

The nodes are joined together by lines, which represent the tasks being carried out between those nodes. The length of each task is shown by the times written in the lower parts of the nodes. Some critical paths have information on each task written underneath the lines that join the nodes, making them easier to read.

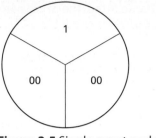

**Figure 3.5** Single event node

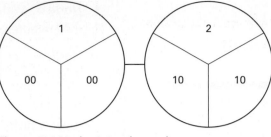

**Figure 3.6** Nodes joined together

On a job, many tasks can be worked on at the same time, e.g. the electricians may be wiring at the same time as the plumber is putting in his pipes. To show this on a critical path, the path can be split.

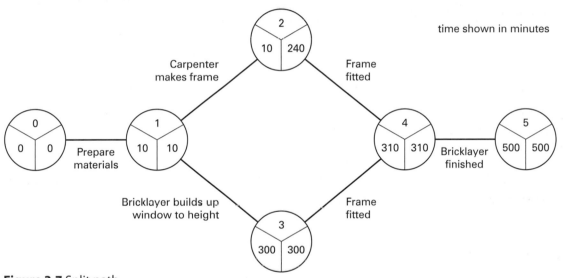

**Figure 3.7** Split path

The example shown shows how a critical path can be used for planning building in a window opening, with a carpenter creating a dummy frame.

The event nodes work as follows:

- **Node 0** – This is the starting point.

- **Node 1** – This is the first task, where the materials are prepared.

- **Node 2** – This is where the carpenter makes the dummy frame for the opening. Notice that the earliest start time is 10 minutes and the last start time is 240 minutes. This means that the carpenter can start building the frame at any time between 10 minutes and 240 minutes into the project. This is because the frame will not be needed until 300 minutes, but the job will only take 60 minutes. If the carpenter starts *after* 240 minutes, there is a possibility that the job may run behind.

- **Node 3** – This is where the bricklayer must be at the site, ready for the frame to be fitted at 300 minutes, or the job will run behind.

> **Activity**
>
> Think of a task you are familiar with and create a critical path for that task.

- **Node 4 –** With the frame fitted, the bricklayer starts at 310 minutes and has until node 5 (500 minutes) to finish.

- **Node 5 –** The job should be completed.

When working with a split path it is vital to remember that certain tasks have to be completed before others can begin. If this is not taken into account on the critical path, the job will run over (which may prove costly, both through penalty clauses and also in terms of the contractor's reputation).

On a large job, it can be easy to misread a critical path as there may be several splits, which could lead to confusion.

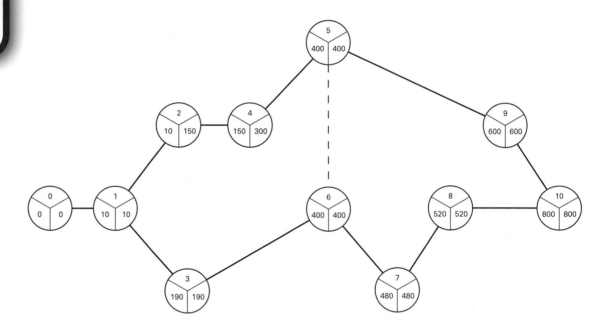

**Figure 3.8** Critical path for a large job

**Remember**

Whichever way you choose to programme your work, your programme must be realistic, with clear objectives and achievable goals.

# FAQ

*How do I know if my job needs planning permission?*

If you are unsure, you should contact your local council.

*What type of planning permission should I apply for?*

If you are unsure of your work, you can make an outline application, which will tell you if your job will pass without getting costly plans made up (though you will have to submit plans later). If you are confident of what you want, you can apply for a full application.

*How much does planning permission cost?*

The costs vary depending on what application you make and to which council you make it.

*Do I need to have all the listed amenities on my building site?*

No. The amenities listed are a guide to what should be on a large site. If you are just doing an extension, the amenities needed will be fewer and simpler (e.g. no site office).

*Which type of programme should I use: bar chart or critical path?*

It is up to the individual which programme they use – both have their good points –  but a bar chart is the easiest to set up and work from.

*What if it rains for the entire 20-day duration of the job?*

The job would be seriously behind schedule. You can't plan for the weather in this country, but it would be unwise to start this job during a rainy season. There are companies that can provide scaffolding with a fitted canopy to protect the work area, which would be ideal for a job of this size. Larger jobs have longer programmes, and when they are drawn up they are made more flexible to allow for a lot of rainy days.

## Knowledge refresher

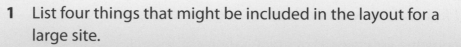

1  List four things that might be included in the layout for a large site.

2  Why is it best to have a good transport route within a site?

3  List four different types of storage that may be needed on a building site.

4  State four pieces of information you can get from a bar chart.

5  With regard to critical paths, what three things are contained in an event node?

## What would you do?

You have been tasked with designing a programme of work for a large contract involving the building of 20 houses. What sort of thing should you check prior to starting? What should you do about plant, labour, materials? What sort of programme should you use (bar or critical path)? What amenities should you consider?

# chapter 4

# Drawings

## OVERVIEW

When drawings are mentioned in the construction industry, people generally tend to think of the architect's drawings and plans that form part of the contract documents. These types of drawings are vital in the construction industry as they form part of the legal contract between client and contractor – and mistakes, either in design or interpretation of the design, can be costly.

However, there are other forms of drawings that are just as important. Setting-out drawings are used to mark out for complex procedures such as constructing cut roofing, staircases or brick arches; and with advances in technology, CAD (computer-aided design) is being used more often.

The Level 2 book gave a good grounding in contract document drawings. This chapter will give you a refresher, and will then expand on your knowledge in this area as well as looking at the wider range of drawings involved in construction today.

This chapter will cover:

- types of drawing
- setting out drawings
- projections
- computer-aided design.

63

# Types of drawing

Plans and drawings are vital to any building work as a way of expressing the client's wishes. Drawings are the best way of communicating a lot of detailed information without the need for pages and pages of text. Drawings form part of the contract documents and go through several stages before they are given to tradespeople for use.

**Stage 1** The client sits down with an architect and explains his/her requirements.

**Stage 2** The architect produces drawings of the work and checks with the client to see if the drawings match what the client wants.

**Stage 3** If required, the drawings go to planning to see if they can be allowed, and are also scrutinised by the Building Regulations Authority. It is at this stage that the drawings may need to be altered to meet Planning or Building Regulations.

**Stage 4** Once passed, the drawings are given to contractors along with the other contract documents, so that they can prepare their tenders for the contract.

**Stage 5** The winning contractor uses the drawings to carry out the job. At this point the drawings will be given to you to work from.

There are three main types of working drawings: location drawings, component drawings and assembly drawings. We will look at each of these in turn.

## Location drawings

Location drawings include:

- **block plans**, which identify the proposed site in relation to the surrounding area. These are usually drawn at a scale of 1:2500 or 1:1250

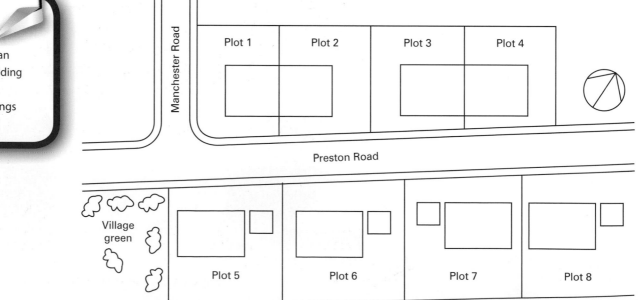

**Figure 4.1** Block plan

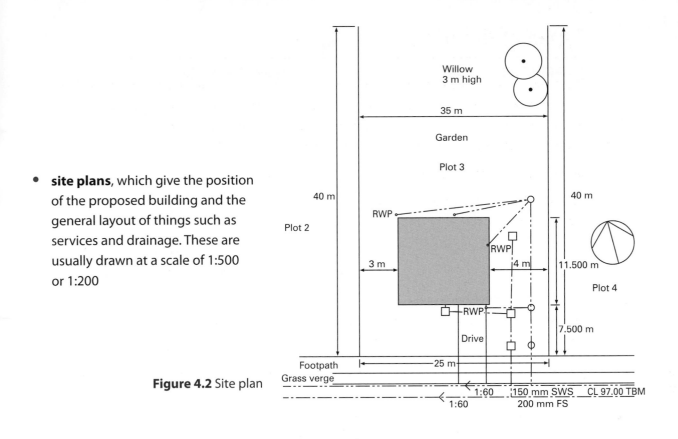

- **site plans**, which give the position of the proposed building and the general layout of things such as services and drainage. These are usually drawn at a scale of 1:500 or 1:200

**Figure 4.2** Site plan

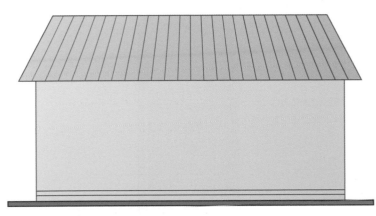

Side elevation

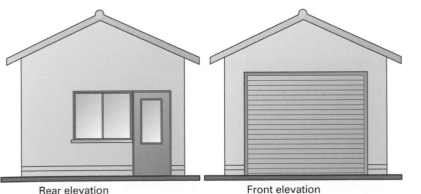

Rear elevation          Front elevation

- **general location drawings**, which show different elevations and sections of the building. These are usually drawn at a scale of 1:200, 1:100 or 1:50

**Figure 4.3** General location drawing

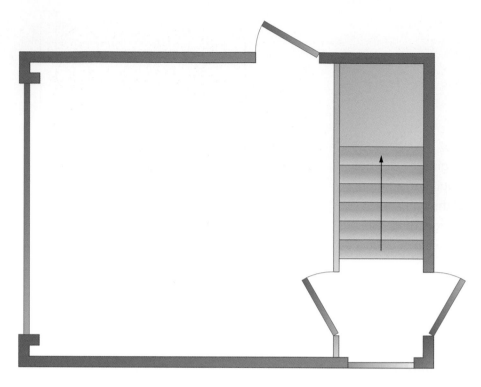

Ground floor plan

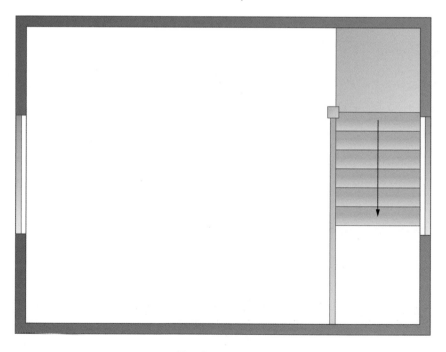

First floor plan

**Figure 4.4** Floor plans

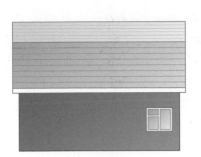
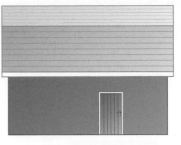

Side elevation        Front elevation        Side elevation

Rear elevation

**Figure 4.5** Elevation drawings

# Component drawings

Component drawings include:

- **range drawings**, which show the different sizes and shapes of a particular range of components. These are usually drawn at a scale of 1:50 or 1:20

## Activity

Produce a component drawing for an item that you are familiar with.

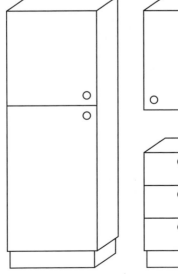
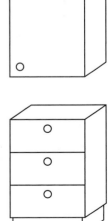
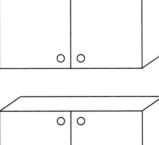
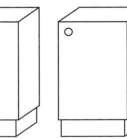

**Figure 4.6** Range drawing

- **detailed drawings**, which show all the information needed to complete or manufacture a component. These are usually drawn at a scale of 1:10, 1:5 or 1:1.

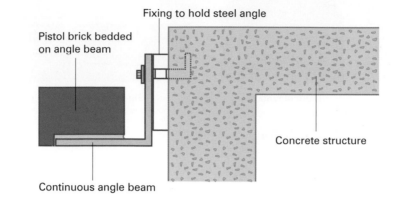

Figure 4.7 Detailed drawing

**Activity**

Produce a detailed drawing of a component you are familiar with.

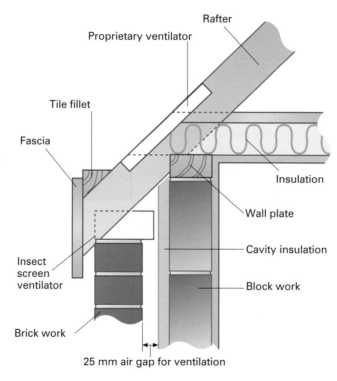

**Figure 4.8** Assembly drawing

## Assembly drawings

Assembly drawings are similar to detailed drawings and show in great detail the various joints and junctions in and between the various parts and components of a building. Assembly drawings are usually drawn at a scale of 1:20, 1:10 or 1:5.

All plans and drawings contain symbols and abbreviations, which are used to show the maximum amount of information in a clear and legible way.

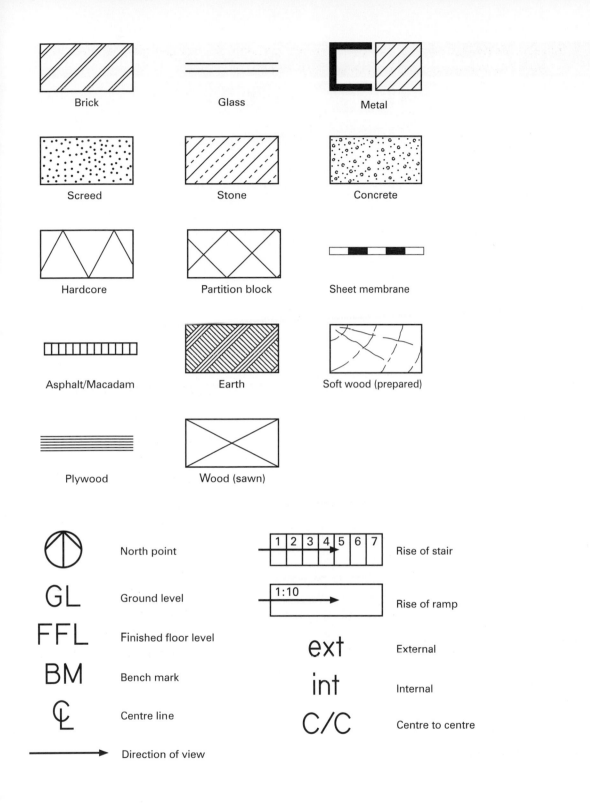

**Figure 4.9** Symbols

| Item | Abbreviation | Item | Abbreviation |
|---|---|---|---|
| Airbrick | AB | Hardcore | hc |
| Asbestos | abs | Hardwood | hwd |
| Bitumen | bit | Insulation | insul |
| Boarding | bdg | Joist | jst |
| Brickwork | bwk | Mild steel | MS |
| Building | bldg | Plasterboard | pbd |
| Cast iron | CI | Polyvinyl acetate | PVA |
| Cement | ct | Polyvinyl chloride | PVC |
| Column | col | Reinforced concrete | RC |
| Concrete | conc | Satin chrome | SC |
| Cupboard | cpd | Satin anodised aluminium | SAA |
| Damp proof course | DPC | Softwood | swd |
| Damp proof membrane | DPM | Stainless steel | SS |
| Drawing | dwg | Tongue and groove | T&G |
| Foundation | fnd | Wrought iron | WI |
| Hardboard | hdbd | | |

**Table 4.1** Abbreviations

# Knowledge refresher

**1** State what happens at the third stage of the client/architect consultation.

**2** What is a suitable scale for a block plan?

**3** Give a suitable scale for a general location drawing.

**4** Describe what a component range drawing is.

# What would you do?

**1** You are working on a job and have received the site plans, which show the layout of the services. You start to dig out for the services and, when you reach the site where the mains gas should be, you find it is not where the drawing shows. What could have caused this problem? What further problems could be caused? What effect could this have financially?

**2** You have been issued a scale drawing for building internal walls, but some of the dimensions are missing. What should you do? What complications could arise from scaling from the drawing as it is? What effect could building a wall in the wrong place have?

# Setting out drawings

Settings out drawings are as important as contract documents. You must be aware of how certain tasks are set out and what drawings can be created to aid in the setting out process.

The setting out drawings are most often needed on smaller jobs, where there is limited or no information from the architect in the form of contract document drawings. Setting out drawings can also be used on larger sites where there has been an alteration or on oversight by the architect.

Here is where the most common forms of setting out drawings are used:

- in carpentry, for cut roofing, where there may be no information on the true lengths of rafters

- in joinery, when setting out for stairs, where there may be no information on the individual rise, etc.

- in bricklaying, where you may come across setting out drawing for arch centres, such as segmental or gothic arches.

Setting out drawings are crucial for creating arches like these

We will now look at a brief example of how roofing and brick arches are set out.

# Finding the true length of a common rafter

Most drawings will tell you the **span** and **rise** of the roof. From these, you can create a drawing that will tell you the true length of the common rafter, and also what angle the ends of the rafter should be cut at.

This true length is the actual length that the rafter needs to be, and all the rafters can be cut to length from the setting out drawing. The setting out drawing for a roof is usually drawn on a sheet of plywood to a scale that fits the sheet.

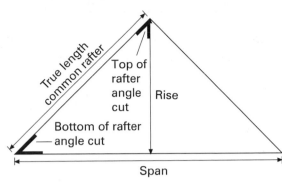

**Figure 4.10** Finding common rafter true length

### Definition

**Span** – the distance measured in the direction of ceiling joists, from the outside of one wall plate to another, known as the overall (O/A) span.

**Rise** – the distance from the top of the wall plate to the roof's peak

# Setting out a segmental brick arch

Most drawings will show you the opening span of the arch, but some may not tell you the radius. Without the radius, you cannot build the arch correctly.

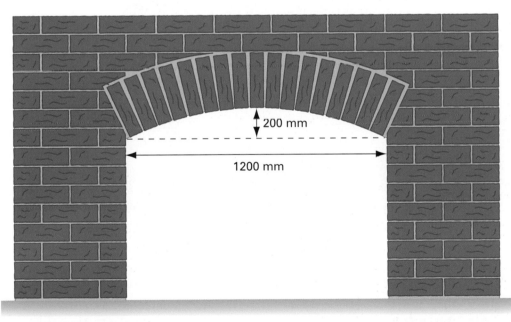

**Figure 4.11** An example of a segmental arch

### Activity

Using a suitable scale, create a setting out drawing for a rafter with a span of 3.5 m and a rise of 1.4 m, so that the true length of the rafter and angles of cuts can be identified.

We will now look at how setting out drawings can aid you in setting out this arch.

**Figure 4.12** Establish the span (a length of 1200 mm has been used here, shown as A–B)

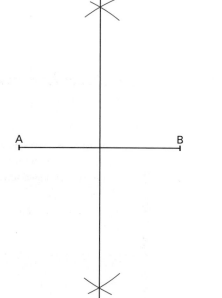

**Figure 4.13** Bisect this line

**Figure 4.14** Establish the rise (the distance from the springing line (A–B) to the highest point of the soffit shown as C). The rise is normally one sixth of the span, so in this case, the rise is shown as 200 mm

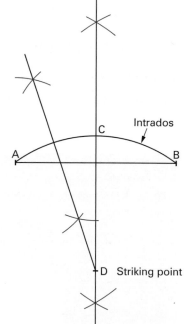

**Figure 4.15** Draw a line from A to C and bisect this line. The point where this bisecting line crosses the bisecting line of the span will be the striking point for the arch (shown here as point D). From striking point D open out compass to point A and draw an arc across to point B. This will provide the intrados for the arch.

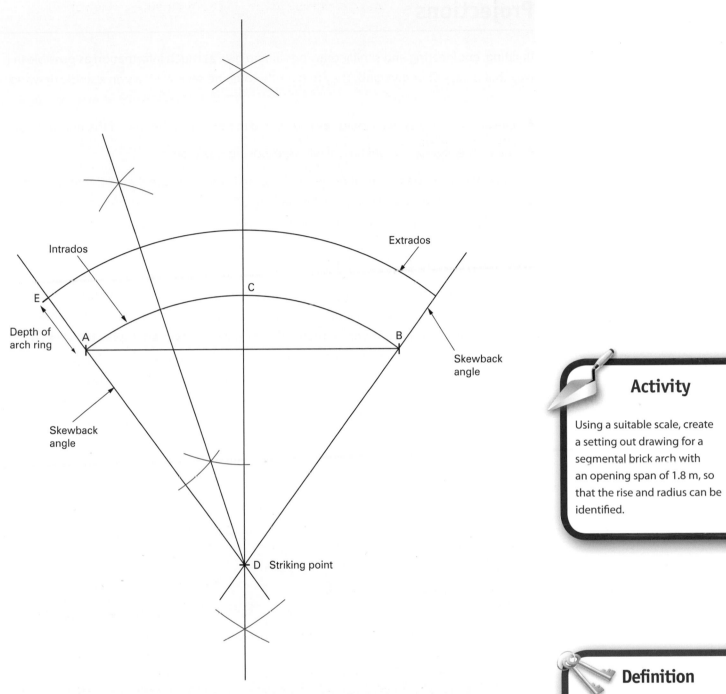

**Figure 4.16** Draw a line from D through A and a line from D through B. These lines will provide the angle for the **skewbacks**. From point A establish depth of arch ring (point E) above point A along line A–D. Set compass from point D to point E and draw an arch. This will provide the exrados.

Setting out for a segmental arch can again be drawn out on a sheet of plywood but, in this case, it can be drawn full size, with the drawing being cut out and used as a template for the arch centre.

**Activity**

Using a suitable scale, create a setting out drawing for a segmental brick arch with an opening span of 1.8 m, so that the rise and radius can be identified.

**Definition**

**Skewbacks** – the angle at the springing point at which the arch rings will be laid

# Projections

Building, engineering and similar drawings aim to give as much information as possible in a way that is easy to understand. They frequently combine several views on a single drawing. These may be of two kinds:

- elevation – the view we would see if we stood in front or to the side of the finished building

- plan – the view we would have if we were looking down on it.

The view we see depends on where we are looking from. There are then different ways of 'projecting' what we would see onto the drawings. The three main methods of projection, used on standard building drawings, are orthographic, isometric and oblique.

## Orthographic projection

Orthographic projection works as if parallel lines were drawn from every point on a model of the building on to a sheet of paper held up behind it (an elevation view), or laid out underneath it (plan view). There are then different ways that we can display the views on a drawing. The method most commonly used in the building industry, for detailed construction drawings, is called 'third angle projection'. In this the front elevation is roughly central. The plan view is drawn directly below the front elevation and all other elevations are drawn in line with the front elevation. An example is shown in Figure 4.17.

Front Elevation

Side Elevation

**Figure 4.17** Orthographic projection

## Isometric projection

In isometric views, the object is drawn at an angle where one corner of the object is closest to the viewer. Vertical lines remain vertical but horizontal lines are drawn at an angle of 30° to the horizontal. This can be seen in Figure 4.18.

**Activity**

Using isometric projection, sketch a component that you are familiar with.

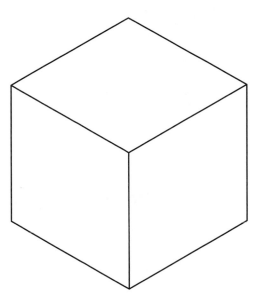

**Figure 4.18** Isometric projection

## Oblique projection

Oblique projection is similar to an isometric view, with the object drawn at an angle where one corner of the object is closest to the viewer. Vertical lines remain vertical but horizontal lines are drawn at an angle of 45° to the horizontal. This can be seen in Figure 4.19.

**Activity**

Using oblique projection, sketch a component that you are familiar with.

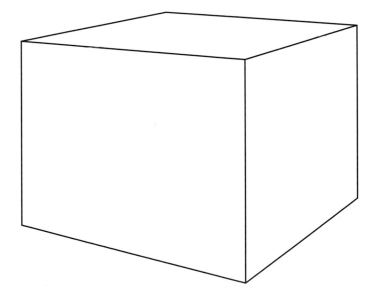

**Figure 4.19** Oblique projection

## Knowledge refresher

1   What is the purpose of setting out drawings?

2   What are the main types of projection used in construction drawings?

3   In isometric projection, at what angle are the horizontal lines drawn?

## What would you do?

You have been tasked with building a segmental brick arch, but there is minimal information on the drawing. You decide to just build the arch but soon run into problems with the radius. What could have prevented the problems? What should you do now? What effect can this have on the building and profitability of the job?

# Computer-aided design

Computer-aided design (CAD) is a system in which a draftsperson uses computer technology to help design a part, product or whole building. It is both a visual and symbol-based method of communication, with conventions particular to a specific technical field.

CAD is used particularly at the drafting stage. Drafting can be done in two dimensions (2-D) and three dimensions (3-D).

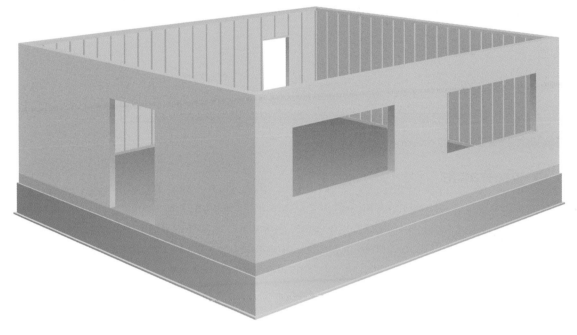

**Figure 4.20** A CAD drawing

CAD is one of the many tools used by engineers and designers, and is used in many ways, depending on the profession of the user and the type of software in question.

There are several types of CAD. Each requires the operator to think differently about how he or she will use it, and he or she must design their virtual components in a different manner for each.

Many companies produce lower-end 2-D systems, and a number of free and open source programs are available. These make the drawing process easier, because there are no concerns about the scale and placement on the drawing sheet that accompanied hand drafting – these can simply be adjusted as required during the creation of the final draft.

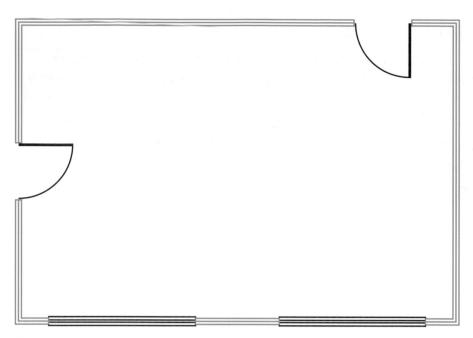

**Figure 4.21** A 2-D CAD drawing

## 3-D wireframe

3D wireframe is in essence an extension of 2-D drafting. Each line has to be manually inserted into the drawing. The final product has no mass properties associated with it, and cannot have features directly added to it, such as holes. The operator approaches these in a similar fashion to the 2-D systems, although many 3-D systems allow you to use the wireframe model to make the final engineering drawing views.

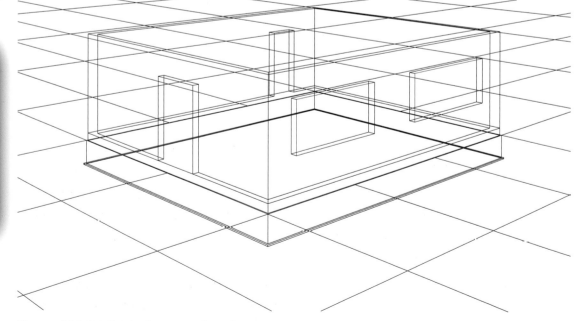

**Figure 4.22** A 3-D wireframe produced using CAD

## 3-D dumb solids

3D 'dumb' solids are created in a way corresponding to manipulations of real-world objects. Basic three-dimensional geometric forms (prisms, cylinders, spheres, and so on) have solid volumes added to or subtracted from them, as if assembling or cutting real-world objects. Two-dimensional projected views can easily be generated from the models. The sorts of basic 3-D solids that are created do not usually include tools to easily allow motion of components, set limits to their motion, or identify interference between components.

**Figure 4.23** A 3-D view of a house produced using CAD

## Top-end systems

Top-end systems offer the capabilities to incorporate more organic, aesthetic and ergonomic features into designs. Freeform surface modelling is often combined with solids to allow the designer to create products that fit the human form and visual requirements, as well as the interface with the machine.

CAD has become an especially important technology within the scope of computer-aided technologies, with benefits such as lower product development costs and a greatly shortened design cycle. CAD enables designers to lay out and develop work on screen, print it out and save it for future editing, saving time on their drawings.

## Knowledge refresher

1   What is CAD?

2   Describe a 3-D wireframe program.

3   Describe a 3-D dumb solids program.

4   What are the main advantages of using a CAD system?

# chapter 5

# Building methods and construction technologies

## OVERVIEW

Whatever type of building you may be involved in constructing, there are certain elements that must be included and certain principles that must be followed. For example, a block of flats and a warehouse will both have foundations, a roof, and so on.

At Level 2, you learned about the basic elements of a building. In this chapter, you will look in greater depth at the main elements and principles of building work and the materials used.

This chapter should be read in conjunction with Chapter 6, which looks specifically at the energy efficiency and sustainability of different building methods and materials.

This chapter will cover:

- foundations
- exterior walls
- internal walls
- floors
- roofs.

Insulation, which is now an important aspect of walls, flooring and roofing, is dealt with in Chapter 6.

# Foundations

Any building work will start with the foundations. The design of any foundation will depend on a number of factors including ground conditions, soil type, the location of drains and trees in relation to the building, and any loads that may be generated, either by the structure or naturally.

## The purpose of foundations

A building damaged through subsidence

The foundations of a building ensure that all **dead** and **imposed loads** are safely absorbed and transmitted through to the natural foundation or sub-soils on which the building is constructed. Failure to adequately absorb and transmit these loads will result in the stability of the building being compromised, and will undoubtedly cause structural damage.

Foundations must also be able to allow for ground movement brought about by the soil shrinking as it dries out and expanding as it becomes wet. The severity of shrinkage or expansion depends on the type of soil you are building on.

Frost may also affect ground movement, particularly in soils that hold water for long periods. When this retained water freezes, it can make the sub-soil expand.

Tree roots and future excavations can also cause movement that affects the sub-soil.

## Types of soil

As you can imagine there are many different types of soils. For foundation design purposes, these have been categorised as follows:

- rock
- gravel
- clay
- sand
- silt.

Each of these categories of sub-soil can be broken down even further: for example,

- clay which is sandy and very soft in its composition
- clay which is sandy but very stiff in its composition.

This information will be of most interest to the architect, but nonetheless is of the utmost importance when designing the foundation.

A number of calculations are used to determine the size and make-up of the foundation. These calculations take into account the **load-bearing capacity of the subsoil**. Calculations for some of the more common types of foundations can be found in the current *Building Regulations*. However, these published calculations cannot possibly cover all situations. Ultimately it will be down to the expertise of the building design teams to accurately calculate the bearing capacity of soils and the make-up of the foundation.

In the early stages of the design process, before any construction work begins, a site investigation will be carried out to ascertain any conditions, situations or surrounding sites which may affect the proposed construction work. A great deal of data will need to be established during site investigations, including:

- position of boundary fences and hedges
- location and depth of services, including gas, electricity, water, telephone cables, drains and sewers
- existing buildings which need to be demolished or protected
- position, height, girth and spread of trees
- types of soil and the depths of these various soils.

The local authorities will normally provide information relating to the location of services, existing buildings, planning restrictions, preservation orders and boundary demarcation. However, all of these will still need to be identified and confirmed through the site investigation. In particular, hidden services will need to be located with the use of modern electronic surveying equipment.

**Definition**

**Load-bearing capacity of subsoil** – the load that can be safely carried by the soil without any adverse settlement

**Find out**

Look at the different methods and equipment used to locate and identify various hidden services.

Soil investigations are critical. Samples of the soil are taken from various points around the site and tested for their composition and for any contamination. Some soils contain chemicals that can seriously damage the foundation concrete. These chemicals include sodium and magnesium sulphates. The effects of these chemicals on the concrete can be counteracted with the use of sulphate-resistant cements.

Many different tests can be carried out on soil. Some are carried out on site; others need to be carried out in laboratories. Tests on soil include:

- penetration tests – to establish density of soil
- compression tests – to establish shear strength of the soil or its load-bearing capacity
- various laboratory tests – to establish particle size, moisture content, humus content and chemical content.

Once all site investigations have been completed and all necessary information and data has been established in relation to the proposed building project, site clearance can take place.

## Site clearance

The main purpose of site clearance is to remove existing buildings, waste, vegetation and, most importantly, the surface layer of soil referred to as topsoil. It is necessary to remove this layer of soil, as it is unsuitable to build on. This surface layer of soil is difficult to compact down due to the high content of vegetable matter, which makes the composition of the soil soft and loose. The topsoil also contains various chemicals that encourage plant growth, which may adversely affect some structures over time.

The process of removing the topsoil can be very costly, in terms of both labour and transportation. The site investigations will determine the volume of topsoil that needs to be removed.

In some instances, the excavated topsoil may not be transported off site. Where building projects include garden plots, the topsoil may just need to be stored on site, thus reducing excessive labour and transportation costs. However, where this is the case, the topsoil must be stored well away from areas where

Removing soil from a site

buildings are to be erected or materials are to be stored, to prevent contamination of soils or materials.

Once the site clearance is complete, excavations for the foundations can start.

## Trench excavation

In most modern-day construction projects, trenches are excavated by mechanical means. Although this is an expensive method, it reduces labour time and the risks associated with manual excavation work. Even with the use of machines to carry out excavations, an element of manual labour will still be needed to clean up the excavation work: loose soil from both the base and sides of the trench will have to be removed, and the sides of the trench will have to be finished vertically.

Manual labour is still required for excavating trenches on some projects where machine access is limited and where only small strip foundations of minimum depths are required.

Trenches to be excavated are identified by lines attached to and stretched between profiles. This is the most accurate method of ensuring trenches are dug to the exact widths.

Excavation work must be carefully planned as workers are killed or seriously injured every year while working in and around trenches. Thorough risk assessments need to be carried out and method statements produced prior to any excavation work commencing.

Potential hazards are numerous and include: possible collapse of the sides of the trench, hitting hidden services, plant machinery falling into the trench and people falling into the trench.

One main cause of trench collapse is the poor placement of materials near to sides of the trench. Not only can materials cause trench collapse, but they may also fall into the trench onto workers. Materials should not be stored near to trenches. Where there is a need to place materials close to the trench for use in the trench itself, always ensure these are kept to a minimum, stacked correctly and used quickly and, most importantly, ensure the trench sides are supported.

Trenches are often excavated by mechanical means

## Activity

Using sketches, show the different ways of supporting trench excavations.

## Trench support

The type and extent of support required in an excavated trench will depend predominantly on the depth of the trench and the stability of the subsoil.

Traditionally, trench support was provided just by using varying lengths and sizes of timber, which can easily be cut to required lengths. However, timber can become unreliable under certain loadings, pressures and weather conditions and can fail in its purpose.

More modern types of materials have been introduced as less costly and time-consuming methods of providing the required support. These materials include steel sheeting, rails and props. Trench support can be provided with a mixture of both timber and steel components.

Here you can see the methods of providing support in trenches with differing materials and a combination of these materials.

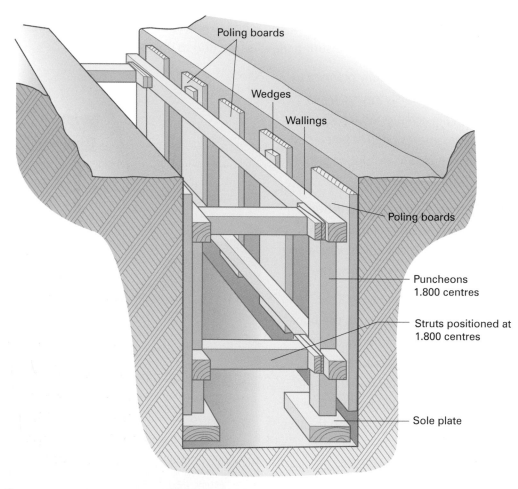

**Figure 5.1** Timber used in trench support

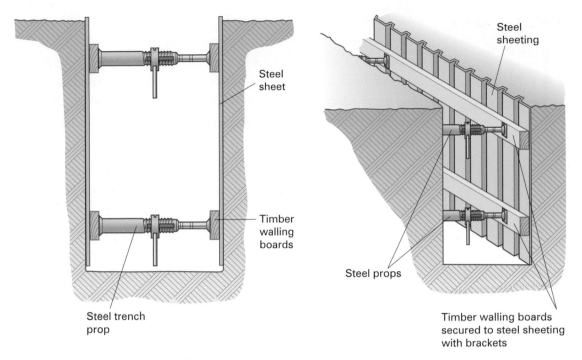

Steel
sheeting

Steel
sheet

Timber
walling
boards

Steel props

Steel trench
prop

Timber walling boards
secured to steel sheeting
with brackets

**Figure 5.2** Combination of timber and steel used in trench support

The amount of timber or other materials required to provide adequate temporary support will be determined by the characteristics of the soil and the soil's ability to remain stable during the time over which the work is carried out. The atmospheric conditions will also affect the soil's ability to remain stable. The longer the soil is exposed to the natural elements, the more chance there is of the soil shrinking or expanding.

Without support, soil will have a natural angle of repose: in other words, the angle at which the soil will rest without collapsing or moving. Again, this will be affected by the natural elements to which the soil is exposed. It is virtually impossible to accurately establish the exact angle at which a type of soil will settle, so it is always advisable to provide more support than is actually required.

Site engineers will carry out calculations in relation to the support requirements for trenches.

Temporary barriers or fences should also be provided around the perimeters of all trenches, to prevent people falling into the trenches and also to prevent materials from being knocked into them. Good trench support methods will incorporate extended trench side supports, which provide a barrier – similar to a toe board on a scaffold – to prevent materials being kicked or knocked into the trench. Where barriers or fences are impractical, then trenches should be covered with suitable sheet materials.

In addition to the supports already mentioned, any services which run through the excavated trenches (in particular drains and gas pipes) need to be supported, especially where the ground has to be excavated underneath them.

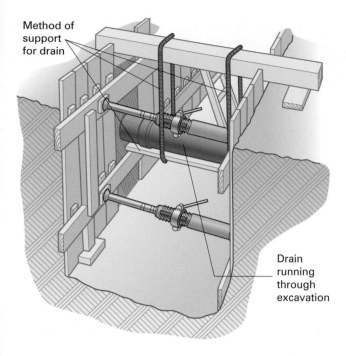

Method of support for drain

Drain running through excavation

**Figure 5.3** Support for drains running through an excavation

Where trenches have to be excavated close to existing buildings, it may be necessary to provide support to the elevation adjacent to the excavation. This is due to the fact that, as ground is taken away from around the existing foundations, the loads will not be adequately and evenly distributed and absorbed into the natural or sub-foundation, possibly causing the structure to collapse. This support is known as shoring.

One other factor that can affect the safety of workers in excavations and the stability of the soil is surface water. Surface water can be found at varying levels within the soil and, depending on the depth, trenches can easily cause flooding. Where this occurs, water pumps will need to be used to keep the trench clear. Failure to keep the trench free of water during construction will not only make operations difficult, but may also weaken and loosen the support systems due to soil displacement.

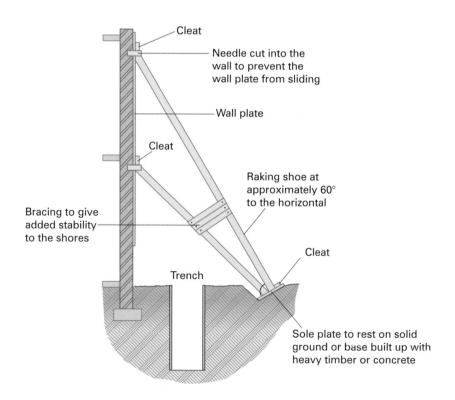

Cleat

Needle cut into the wall to prevent the wall plate from sliding

Wall plate

Cleat

Raking shoe at approximately 60° to the horizontal

Bracing to give added stability to the shores

Cleat

Trench

Sole plate to rest on solid ground or base built up with heavy timber or concrete

**Figure 5.4** Raking shores used to support an existing building

# Types of foundation

As previously stated, the design of a foundation will be down to the architect and structural design team. The final decision on the suitability and depth of the foundation, and on the thickness of the concrete, will rest with the local authority's building control department.

## Strip foundations

The most commonly used strip foundation is the 'narrow strip' foundation, which is used for small domestic dwellings and low-rise structures. Once the trench has been excavated, it is filled with concrete to within 4–5 courses of the ground level DPC. The level of the concrete fill can be reduced in height, but this makes it difficult for the bricklayer due to the confined area in which to lay bricks or blocks.

The depth of this type of foundation must be such that the subsoil acting as the natural foundation cannot be affected by the weather. This depth would normally not be less than 1 m.

The narrow strip foundation is not suitable for buildings with heavy structural loading or where the subsoil is weak in terms of supporting the combined loads imposed on it. Where this is the case, a wide strip foundation is needed.

## Wide strip foundations

Wide strip foundations consist of steel reinforcement placed within the concrete base of the foundation. This removes the need to increase the depth considerably in order to spread the heavier loads adequately.

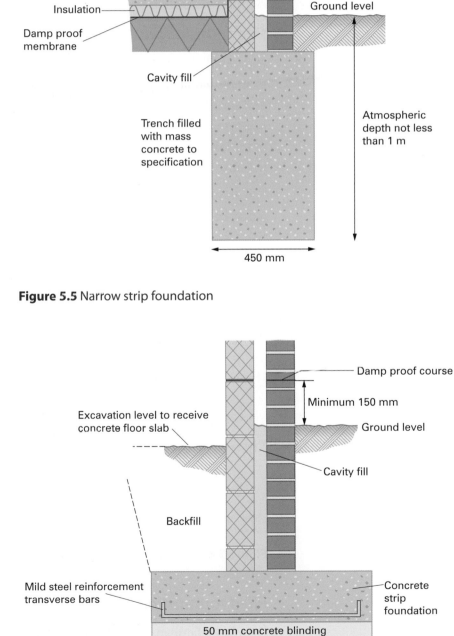

**Figure 5.5** Narrow strip foundation

**Figure 5.6** Wide strip foundation

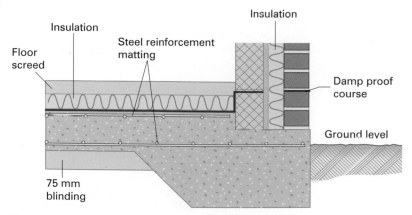

**Figure 5.7** Raft foundation

# Raft foundations

These types of foundation are used where the soil has poor bearing capacity, making the soil prone to settlement. A raft foundation consists of a slab of reinforced concrete covering the entire base of the structure. The depth of the concrete is greater around the edges of the raft in order to protect the load-bearing soil directly beneath the raft from further effects of moisture taken in from the surrounding area.

## Pad foundations

Pad foundations are used where the main loads of a structure are imposed at certain points. An example would be where brick or steel columns support the weight of floors or roof members, and walls between the columns are of non-load-bearing cladding panels. The simplest form of pad foundation is where individual concrete pads are placed at various points around the base of the structure, and concrete ground beams span across them. The individual concrete pads will absorb the main imposed loads, while the beams will help support the walls.

The depth of a pad foundation will depend on the load being imposed on it; in some instances, it may be necessary to use steel reinforcement to prevent excessive depths of concrete. This type of pad foundation can reduce the amount of excavation work required, as trenches do not need to be dug out around the entire base of the proposed structure.

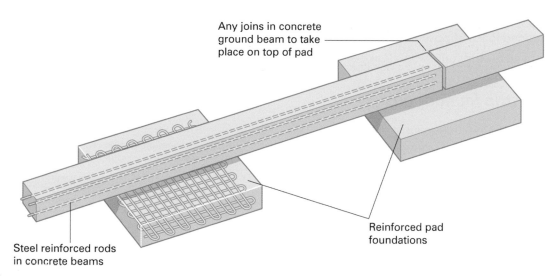

**Figure 5.8** Square pad foundation with spanning ground beams

## Piled foundations

There are a large number of different types of piled foundations, each with an individual purpose in relation to the type of structure and ground conditions.

*Short bored piled foundations* are the most common piled foundations. They are predominantly used for domestic buildings where the soil is prone to movement, particularly at depths below 1 m.

A series of holes are bored, by mechanical means, around the perimeter of the base of the proposed building. The diameter of the bored holes will normally be between 250 and 350 mm and can extend to depths of up to 4 m. Once the holes have been bored, shuttering is constructed to form lightweight reinforced concrete beams, which span across the bored piles. The bored holes are then filled with concrete, with reinforcement projecting from the top of the pile concrete, so it can be incorporated into the concrete beams that span the piles.

As with the pad foundation, short bored piled foundations can significantly reduce the amount of excavated soil because there is no need to excavate deep trenches around the perimeter of the proposed structure.

## Stepped foundations

A stepped foundation is used on sloping ground. The height of each step should not be greater than the thickness of the concrete, and should not be greater than 450 mm. Where possible, the height of the step should coincide with brick course height in order to avoid oversized mortar bed joints and eliminate the need for split brick courses. The overlap of the concrete to that below should not be less than 300 mm or less than the thickness of the concrete.

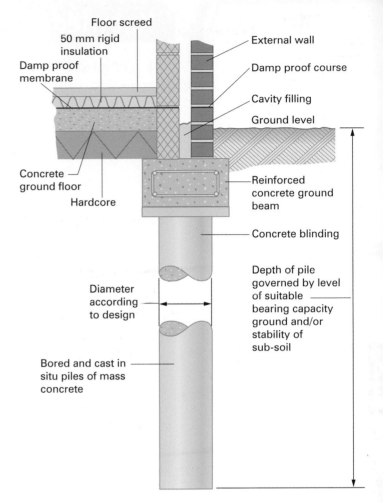

**Figure 5.9** Typical short bored piled foundation

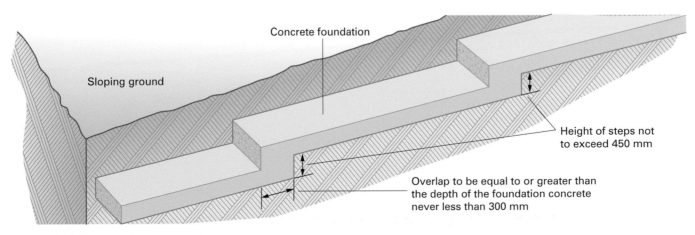

**Figure 5.10** Typical stepped foundation

## Activity

Sketch the following different types of foundation:

- strip foundation
- wide strip foundation
- raft foundation
- pad foundation
- piled foundation
- stepped foundation.

## Knowledge refresher

1 What should happen before any construction work commences on a building project?

2 State three factors that influence the design of a foundation.

3 Explain what is meant by a 'dead load'.

4 Explain what is meant by an 'imposed load'.

5 During a site investigation, certain data need to be collected. Name three types of data that have to be recorded.

6 Why must excavation work be carefully planned before it is carried out?

7 Name three categories of soil.

8 Name three types of foundation.

9 How can surface water affect excavation work?

10 In a stepped foundation, what is the recommended maximum height of each concrete step?

# What would you do?

1   You have been tasked with building a garage. You decide not to go with a soil survey as this is an extra expense, and you just put in a standard strip foundation. What could go wrong? What could the cost implications be? What other implications could there be?

2   You have been asked by your boss to enter an excavation to clean out some loose soil. The excavation is 1.5 m deep, and has been excavated for a foundation. There are no supports on the excavation sides and overnight there has been a considerable amount of rainfall. Your boss shouts at you to get on with it as the concrete for the foundation will be here in 10 minutes. What should you do? What could the implications be if you do it? What could the implications be if you don't?

# Exterior walls

External walls come in a variety of types, but the most common is cavity walling. Cavity walling is simply two masonry walls built parallel to each other, with a gap between acting as the cavity. The cavity wall acts as a barrier to weather, with the outer leaf preventing rain and wind penetrating the inner leaf. The cavity is usually filled with insulation to prevent heat loss.

## How cavity walls are constructed

Cavity walls mainly consist of a brick outer skin and a blockwork inner skin. There are instances where the outer skin may be made of block and then rendered or covered by tile hanging. The minimum cavity size allowed is 75 mm but the cavity size is normally governed by the type and thickness of insulation to be used and whether the cavity is to be fully filled or partially filled with insulation.

The thickness of blocks used will also govern the overall size of the cavity wall. On older properties, the internal blocks were always of 100 mm thickness. Nowadays, due to the emphasis on energy conservation and efficiency, blocks are more likely to be 125 mm or more.

In all cases, the cavity size will be set out to the drawing with overall measurements specified by the architect and to local authority requirements.

Once the **foundations** have been concreted the **sub-structural walling** can be constructed, usually by using blocks for both walls (see Figure 5.11).

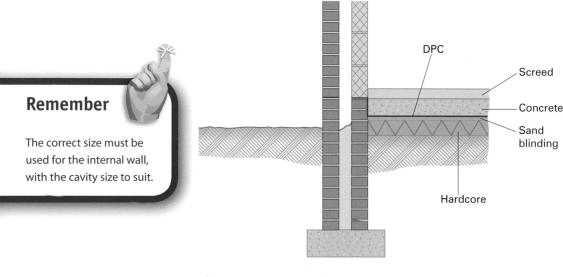

**Figure 5.11** Section of sub-structural walling

In some situations trench blocks may be used below ground level and then traditional cavity work constructed up to the damp proof course (DPC). A horizontal DPC must be inserted at a minimum height of 150 mm above ground level to both walls. This is to prevent damp rising, below ground, up through the block and brickwork to penetrate to the inside. The cavity must also be filled with weak concrete to ground level to help the sub-structural walling resist lateral pressure.

## Cavity walls above DPC

The older, traditional way to build a cavity wall is to build the brickwork first and then the blockwork. Now, due to the introduction of insulation into the cavity, the blockwork is generally built first, especially when the cavity is partially filled with insulation. This is because the insulation requires holding in place against the internal block wall, by means of special clips that are attached to the **wall ties**. In most cases the clips are made of plastic as they do not rust or rot. The reason for clipping the insulation is to stop it from moving away from the blocks, which would cause the loss of warmth to the interior of the building, as well as causing a possible **bridge** of the cavity, which could cause a damp problem.

The brick courses should be gauged at 75 mm per course but sometimes course sizes may change slightly to accommodate window or door heights. In most instances these positions and measurements are designed to work to the standard gauge size. This will also allow the blockwork to run level at every third course of brick, although the main reason will be explained in the wall tie section below.

On most large sites, patent types of corner profile are used rather than building traditional corners (see Figure 5.12). These allow the brickwork to be built faster and, if set up correctly, more accurately. But they must also be marked for the gauge accurately and it makes sense to mark window sill heights or **window heads** and door heights so they do not get missed, which would result in brickwork being taken down.

### Activity

Sketch a section through a cavity wall including DPC and wall ties.

### Definition

**Wall ties** – stainless steel or plastic fixings to tie cavity walls together

**Bridge** – where moisture can be transferred from the outer wall to the inner leaf by material touching both walls

**Window head** – top of a window

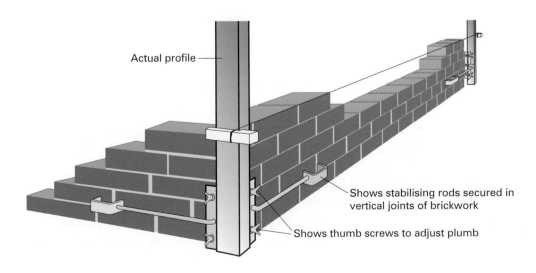

Actual profile

Shows stabilising rods secured in vertical joints of brickwork

Shows thumb screws to adjust plumb

**Figure 5.12** A corner profile set up

## Wall ties

Wall ties are a very important part of a cavity wall as they tie the internal and external walls together, resulting in a stronger job. If we built cavity walls to any great height without connecting them together, the walls would be very unstable and could possibly collapse.

A wall tie should be:

1.  rust-proof

2.  rot-proof

3.  of sufficient strength

4.  able to resist moisture.

There are many designs of wall tie currently on the market, with a wide selection suitable for all types of construction methods. One of the most common types used when tying together brick and block leaves is the masonry general purpose tie. These ties are made from very strong stainless steel, and incorporate a twist in the steel at the mid point of the length. This twist forms a drip system, which prevents the passage of water from the outer to the inner leaf of the structure.

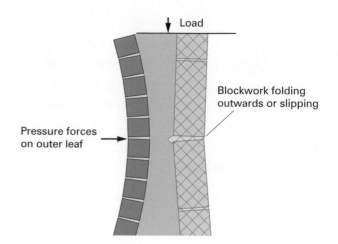

Load

Blockwork folding outwards or slipping

Pressure forces on outer leaf

**Figure 5.13** Section of wall without wall ties

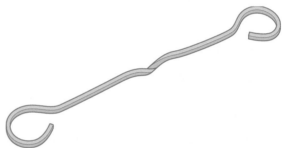

**Figure 5.14** General purpose wall tie

You must take care to keep the wall ties clean when they are placed in the wall: if bridging occurs, it may result in moisture penetrating the internal wall.

## The positioning and density of wall ties

In cavity walling where both the outer and inner leaves are 90 mm or thicker, you should use ties at not less than 2.5 per square metre, with 900 mm maximum horizontal distance by a maximum 450 mm vertical distance and staggered.

At positions such as vertical edges of an opening, unreturned or unbonded edges and vertical expansion joints, you need to use additional ties at a maximum of 300 mm in height (usually 225 mm to suit block course height) and located not more than 225 mm from the edge. Wall ties should be bedded into each skin of the cavity wall to a minimum distance of 50 mm.

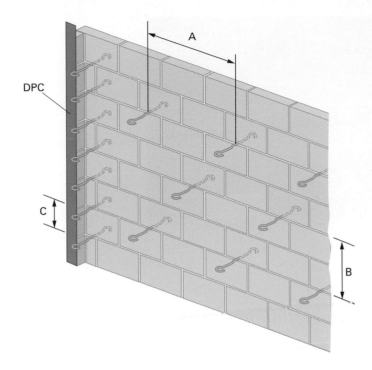

DPC

A

C

B

A  900 mm maximum horizontal distance

B  450 mm maximum vertical distance

C  Additional ties, 300 mm maximum vertical distance

**Figure 5.15** Spacing of wall ties

**Did you know?**

Any batten can be used as long as the width is the same as the cavity space.

**Definition**

**Cavity batten** – a timber piece laid in a cavity to prevent mortar droppings falling down the cavity

## Keeping a cavity wall clean

It is important to keep the cavity clean to prevent dampness. If mortar is allowed to fall to the bottom of the cavity it can build up and allow the damp to cross and enter the building. Mortar can also become lodged on the wall ties and create a bridge for moisture to cross. We can prevent this by the use of **cavity battens**, pieces of timber the thickness of the cavity laid on to the wall ties and attached by wires or string (to prevent dropping down the cavity) to the wall and lifted alternately as the wall progresses.

The bottom of the wall can be kept clean by either leaving bricks out or bedding bricks with sand so they can be taken out to clean the cavity. These are called core holes and are situated every fourth brick along the wall to make it easy to clean out each day. Once the wall is completed the bricks are bedded into place.

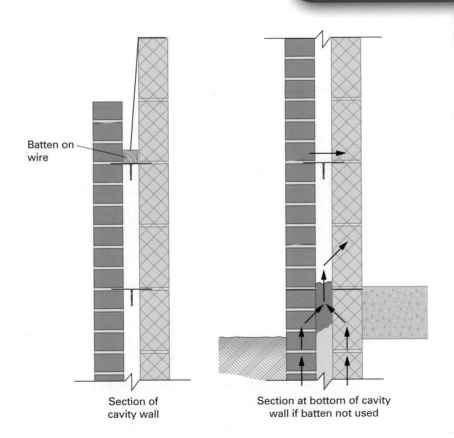

Batten on wire

Section of cavity wall

Section at bottom of cavity wall if batten not used

**Figure 5.16** Cavity batten in use

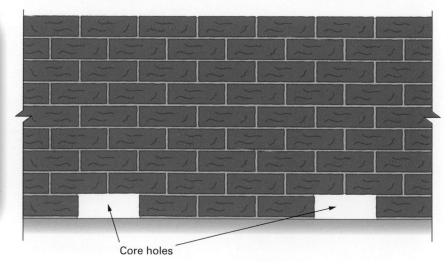

Core holes

Elevation of wall

**Figure 5.17** Core holes

## Steps to take to prevent damp penetration

- Set out openings carefully to avoid awkward bonds.
- Care is needed in construction to make sure dampness or water does not enter the building.
- DPCs and wall ties should be carefully positioned.
- Steel cavity lintels should have minimum 150 mm bearings solidly bedded in the correct position.
- Weep holes should be put in at 450 mm centres immediately above the lintel in the outer leaf.

No insulation has been shown in the drawings because they only show one situation. In most cavity wall construction, insulation of one kind or another will have to be incorporated to satisfy current *Building Regulations*.

## Fire spread

In addition to the prevention of damp penetration and cold bridging, there is a requirement under the *Building Regulations* that cavities and concealed spaces in a structure or fabric of a building are sealed by using cavity barriers or fire stopping. This cuts down the hidden spread of smoke or flames in the event of fire breaking out in a building.

## Closing at eaves level

The cavity walls have to be 'closed off' at roof level for two main reasons:

1. To prevent heat loss and the spread of fire.
2. To prevent birds or vermin entering and nesting.

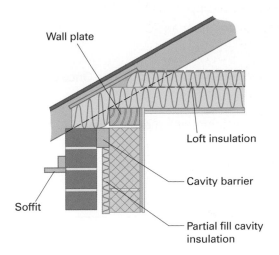

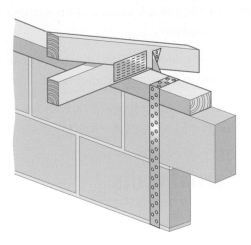

**Figure 5.18** Roof section

This area of the wall is where the roof is connected, by means of a timber wall plate bedded on to the inner leaf. The plate is then secured by means of restraint straps that are galvanised 'L' shaped straps screwed to the top of the wall plate and down the blockwork. This holds the roof structure firmly in place and also prevents the roof from spreading under the weight of the tiles, etc. The minimum distance that the straps should be apart is 1.2 m. In some instances they may be connected directly from the roof truss to the wall.

If a gable wall is required, restraint straps should be used to secure the roof to the end wall (see Figure 5.18).

The external wall can be built to the height of the top of the truss so as not to leave gaps, or 'closed off' by building blocks laid flat to cover the cavity above the external soffit line from inside, avoiding damp penetration. In some instances the cavity may be left open with the cavity insulation used as the seal.

## Timber-kit houses

Timber-kit houses are becoming more and more popular as they can be erected to a windtight and watertight stage within a few days. The principle is similar to a cavity wall, but here the inner skin is a timber frame, which is clad in timber sheet material and covered in a breathable membrane, to prevent water and moisture penetrating the timber. The outer skin is usually face brickwork.

## Constructing timber-kit houses

Timber-kit house construction starts off in exactly the same way as any house build, with the foundations and the cavity wall built up to DPC level. However, from then on, the construction method is completely

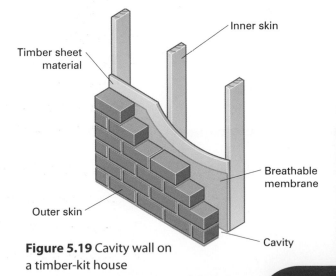

**Figure 5.19** Cavity wall on a timber-kit house

different, as the interior skin of the cavity is timber framed as opposed to block work. The timber-kit house is created in panels within a factory environment and delivered in sections on the back of a lorry.

The timber panels are lifted into place (usually by crane) and are bolted together. Once the wall panels are in place, the exterior face brickwork can begin.

There are also other types of exterior walling, such as solid stone or log cabin style. Industrial buildings may have steel walls clad in sheet metal.

# Internal walls

Internal walls are either load bearing – meaning they support any upper floors or roof – or are non-load-bearing, used to divide the floor space into rooms.

Internal walls also come in a variety of styles. Here is a list of the most common types.

- **Solid block walls** – simple block work, either covered with plasterboard or plastered over to give a smooth finish, to which wallpaper or paint is applied. Solid block walls offer low thermal and sound insulation qualities, but advances in technology and materials means that blocks manufactured from a lightweight aggregate can give better sound and heat insulation.

- **Solid brick walling** – usually made with face brickwork as a decorative finish. It is unusual for all walls within a house to be made from brickwork.

- **Timber stud walling** – more common in timber kit houses and newer buildings. Timber stud walling is also preferred when dividing an existing room, as it is quicker to erect. Clad in plasterboard and plastered to a smooth finish, timber stud partitions can be made more fire resistant and sound/thermal qualities can be improved with the addition of insulation or different types of plasterboard. Another benefit of timber stud walling is that timber noggins can be placed within the stud to give additional fixings for components such as radiators or wall units. Timber stud walling can also be load bearing, in which case thicker timbers are used.

- **Metal stud walling** – similar to timber stud, except metal studs are used and the plasterboard is screwed to the studding.

- **Grounds lats** – timber battens that are fixed to a concrete or stone wall to provide a flat surface, to which plasterboard is attached and a plaster finish applied

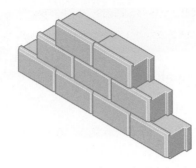

**Figure 5.20** Solid block wall

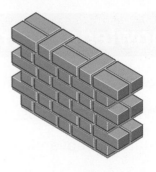

**Figure 5.21** Solid brick wall

**Figure 5.22** Timber stud wall

**Figure 5.23** Metal stud wall

# Knowledge refresher

1 What is the minimum cavity size for a cavity wall?

2 What is the purpose of wall ties in a cavity wall?

3 State one advantage of using a corner profile.

4 What is the main reason a cavity needs to be kept clean?

5 Outline three steps to take to prevent damp penetration in a cavity wall.

6 Give two reasons why cavity walls have to be closed off at roof level.

7 State one advantage of using timber kit as opposed to cavity walling.

8 How are timber panels in a kit house joined together?

9 How could a timber stud wall be made more soundproof?

10 Describe how a solid internal block wall can be finished.

# What would you do?

1 You are going to build your own house. Using the information you gained from previous Activities and what you know, what type of house should you build: cavity or kit?

2 You have been tasked with creating an opening in an internal block work wall. What can you do to check if the wall is load bearing? What should be done if the wall is load bearing? What could the consequences be if the wall is load bearing and you create the opening without shoring?

# Floors

Floors have a number of standard components, including the following:

- **DPC**

This is the damp proof course that is inserted into both skins of the external cavity wall construction. It should be a proprietary product that is tested and has a long life expectancy.

- **DPM**

This is the damp proof membrane, which is placed in large sheets within the floor structure so it can resist the passage of moisture and rising damp. This keeps the floors dry. The DPM should be taken up vertically and tucked into the DPC to form a complete seal. All DPM should be lapped by at least 300 mm, with any joints taped.

- **Screeds**

Floor screeds are considered in the solid concrete floor section (see page 118). They provide a finish to the concrete surface, cover up services and provide a level for floor finishes to be applied to. They also provide falls to floors: for example, in a wet room for the shower waste.

- **Wall plate**

The wall plate is on top of the sleeper wall that supports the floor joists. It has a DPC underneath it to prevent damp penetrating the timber. Wall plates should be treated.

The most common types of flooring used are:

- suspended timber floors
- solid concrete floors
- pre-cast beam floors
- floating floors.

## Suspended timber floors

Suspended timber floors can be fitted at any level, from top floor to ground floor. In the next few pages, you will look at:

- basic structure
- joists
- construction methods
- floor coverings.

## Basic structure

Suspended timber floors are constructed with timbers known as joists, which are spaced parallel to each other spanning the distance of the building. Suspended timber floors are similar to traditional roofs in that they can be single or double, a single floor being supported at the two ends only and a double floor supported at the two ends and in the middle by way of a honeycombed sleeper/dwarf wall, steel beam or load-bearing partition.

All floors must be constructed to comply with the *Building Regulations*, in particular Part C, which is concerned with damp. The bricklayer must insert a **damp proof course (DPC)** between the brick or block work when building the walls, situated no less than 150 mm above ground level. This prevents moisture moving from the ground to the upper side of the floor. No timbers are allowed below the DPC. Air bricks, which are built into the external walls of the building, allow air to circulate round the underfloor area, keeping the moisture content below the dry rot limit of 20 per cent, thus preventing dry rot.

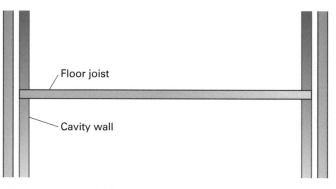

**Figure 5.24** Single floor

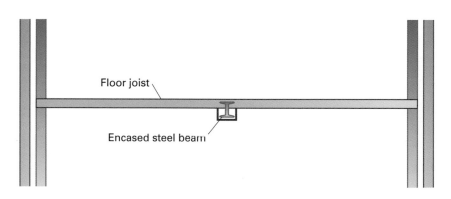

**Figure 5.25** Double floor

## Joists

In domestic dwellings suspended upper floors are usually single floors, with the joist supported at each end by the structural walls but, if support is required, a load-bearing partition is used. The joists that span from one side of the building to the other are called bridging joists, but any joists that are affected by an opening in the floor such as a stairwell or chimney are called trimmer, trimming and trimmed joists.

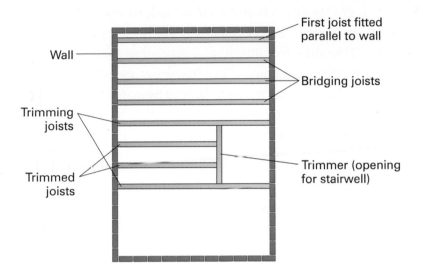

**Figure 5.26** Joists and trimmers

## Types of joist

As well as the traditional method of using solid timber joists, there are now alternatives available. These are the most common.

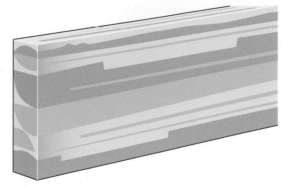

**Figure 5.27** Laminated joist

### Laminated joists

These were originally used for spanning large distances, as a laminated beam could be made to any size, but now they are more commonly used as an environmental alternative to solid timber – recycled timber can be used in the laminating process. They are more expensive than solid timber, as the joists have to be manufactured.

### I type joists

These are now some of the most commonly used joists in the construction industry: they are particularly popular in new build and are the only joists used in timber kit house construction. I type beam joists are lighter and more environmentally friendly as they use a composite panel in the centre, usually made from oriented strand board, which can be made from recycled timber.

The following construction method shows how to fit solid timber joists but whichever joists you use, the methods are the same.

**Figure 5.28** I type joist

## Construction methods

A suspended timber floor must be supported either end. The figures below show ways of doing this.

**(a)** Old practice

Joist

Damp walls affecting timber

Wall plate

**(b)** New practice

TW type hanger

Joist

**Figure 5.29** Solid floor bearings

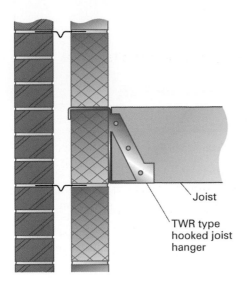

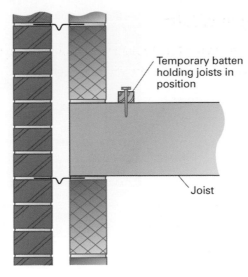

(a) Joist hanger bearing

(b) Built-in bearing

**Figure 5.30** Cavity wall bearings

If a timber floor has to trim an opening, there must be a joint between the trimming and the trimmer joists. Traditionally, a **tusk tenon joint** was used (even now, this is sometimes preferred) between the trimming and the trimmer joist. If the joint is formed correctly a tusk tenon is extremely strong, but making one is time-consuming. A more modern method is to use a metal framing anchor or timber-to-timber joist hanger.

Traditional tusk tenon joint

Joist hanger

## Fitting floor joists

Before the carpenter can begin constructing the floor, the bricklayer needs to build the honeycomb sleeper walls. This type of walling has gaps in each course to allow the free flow of air through the underfloor area. It is on these sleeper walls that the carpenter lays his timber wall plate, which will provide a fixing for the floor joists.

The following pages describe the steps in fitting floor joists.

**Activity**

Sketch a section through a suspended timber floor, showing how the flooring is supported.

**Definition**

**Tusk tenon joint** – a kind of mortise and tenon joint that uses a wedge-shaped key to hold the joint together

**Activity**

With the aid of a sketch, explain the purpose of a joist hanger and how it functions.

**Activity**

Sketch a tusk tenon joint.

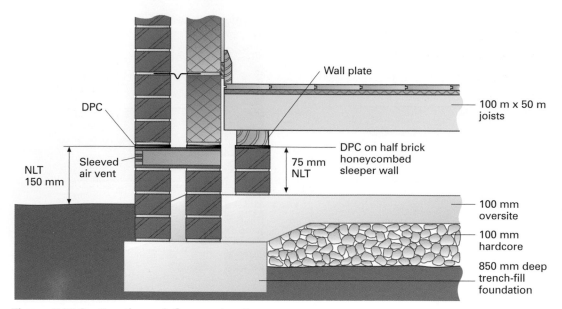

Figure 5.31 Section through floor and wall

**Step 1** Bed and level the wall plate onto the sleeper wall with the DPC under it.

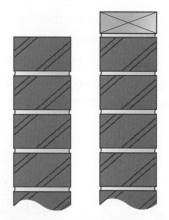

Figure 5.32 Step 1 Bed in the wall plate

**Step 2** Cut joists to length and seal the ends with a coloured preservative. Mark out the wall plate with the required centres, space the joists out and fix temporary battens near each end to hold the joists in position. Ends should be kept away from walls by approximately 12 mm. It is important to ensure that the camber is turned upwards.

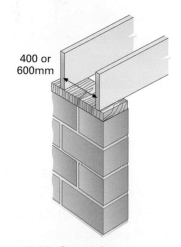

Figure 5.33 Step 2 Space out joists

**Step 3** Fix the first joist parallel to the wall with a gap of 50 mm. Fix trimming and trimmer joists next to maintain the accuracy of the opening.

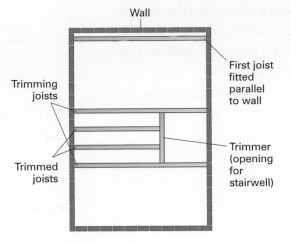

**Figure 5.34 Step 3** Fit first joist and trimmers

**Step 4** Fix subsequent joists at the required spacing as far as the opposite wall. Spacing will depend on the size of joist and/ or floor covering, but usually 400 mm to 600 mm centres are used.

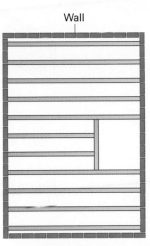

**Figure 5.35 Step 4** Fit remaining joists

**Step 5** Fit folding wedges to keep the end joists parallel to the wall. Overtightening is to be avoided in case the wall is strained.

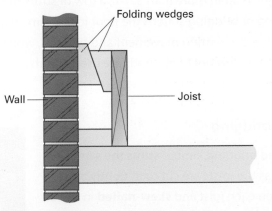

**Figure 5.36 Step 5** Fit folding wedges

**Step 6** Check that the joists are level with a straight edge or line and, if necessary, pack with slate or DPC.

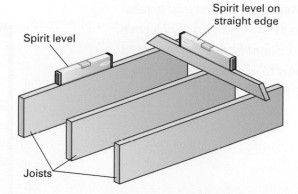

**Figure 5.37  Step 6** Ensure joists are level

**Step 7** Fit restraining straps and, if the joists span more than 3.5 m, fit strutting and bridging, described in more detail next.

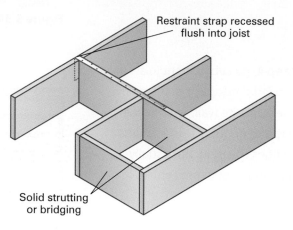

**Figure 5.38  Step 7** Fix restraining straps, struts and bridges

## Strutting and bridging

When joists span more than 3.5 m, a row of struts must be fixed midway between each joist. Strutting or bridging stiffens the floor in the same way that noggins stiffen timber stud partitions, preventing movement and twisting, which is useful when fitting flooring and ceiling covering. A number of methods are used, but the main ones are solid bridging, herringbone strutting and steel strutting.

### Solid bridging

For solid bridging, timber struts the same depth as the joists are cut to fit tightly between each joist and **skew-nailed** in place. A disadvantage of solid bridging is that it tends to loosen when the joists shrink.

Solid bridging

## Herringbone strutting

Here timber battens (usually 50 × 25 mm) are cut to fit diagonally between the joists. A small saw cut is put into the ends of the battens before nailing to avoid the battens splitting. This will remain tight even after joist shrinkage. The following steps describe the fitting of timber herringbone strutting.

**Step 1** Nail a temporary batten near the line of strutting to keep the joists spaced at the correct centres.

Space joists

**Step 2** Mark the depth of a joist across the edge of the two joists, then measure 12 mm inside one of the lines and remark the joists. The 12 mm less than the depth of the joist ensures that the struts will finish just below the floor and ceiling level (as shown in step 5).

Mark joist depths

**Step 3** Lay the strut across two joists at a diagonal to the lines drawn in Step 2.

Lay struts across two joists at a diagonal

**Step 4** Draw a pencil line underneath as shown in Step 3 and cut to the mark. This will provide the correct angle for nailing.

Cut to the mark

**Step 5** Fix the strut between the two joists. The struts should finish just below the floor and ceiling level. This prevents the struts from interfering with the floor and ceiling if movement occurs.

Fix the strut

### Steel strutting

There are two types of galvanised steel herringbone struts available.

The first has angled lugs for fixing with the minimum 38 mm round head wire nails.

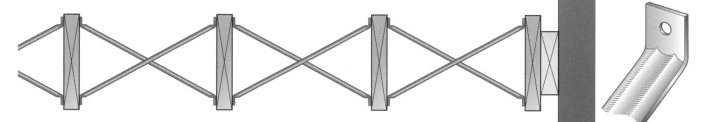

**Figure 5.39** Catric® steel joist struts

The second has pointed ends, which bed themselves into joists when forced in at the bottom and pulled down at the top. Unlike other types of strutting, this type is best fixed from below.

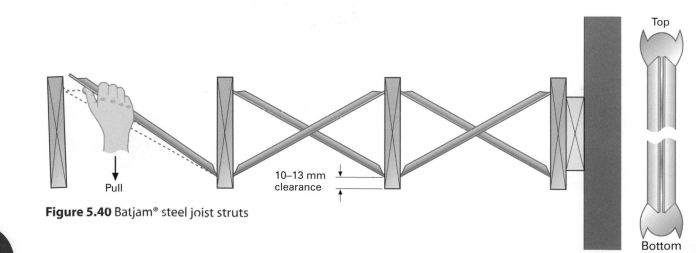

**Figure 5.40** Batjam® steel joist struts

The disadvantage of steel strutting is that it only comes in set sizes, to fit centres of 400, 450 and 600 mm. This is a disadvantage as there will always be a space in the construction of a floor that is smaller than the required centres.

## Restraint straps

Anchoring straps, normally referred to as restraint straps, are needed to restrict any possible movement of the floor and walls due to wind pressure. They are made from galvanised steel, 5 mm thick for horizontal restraints and 2.5 mm for vertical restraints, 30 mm wide and up to 1.2 m in length. Holes are punched along the length to provide fixing points.

When the joists run parallel to the walls, the straps will need to be housed into the joist to allow the strap to sit flush with the top of the joist, keeping the floor even. The anchors should be fixed at a maximum of 2 m centre to centre. More information can be found in schedule 7 of the *Building Regulations*.

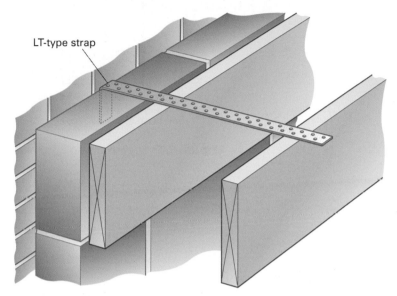

**Figure 5.41** Restraint straps for joists parallel or at right angles to a wall

## Floor coverings

## Softwood flooring

Softwood flooring can be used at either ground or upper floor levels. It usually consists of 25 × 150 mm tongued and grooved (T&G) boards. The tongue is slightly off centre to provide extra wear on the surface that will be walked upon.

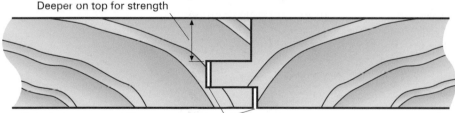

**Figure 5.42** Section through softwood covering

When boards are joined together, the joints should be staggered evenly throughout the floor to give it strength. They should never be placed next to each other, as this prevents the joists from being tied together properly. The boards are either fixed with floor brads nailed through the surface and punched below flush, or secret nailed with lost head nails through the tongue. The nails used should be 2½ times the thickness of the floorboard.

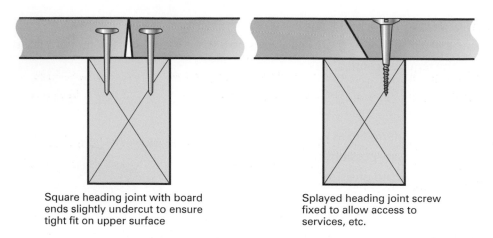

Square heading joint with board ends slightly undercut to ensure tight fit on upper surface

Splayed heading joint screw fixed to allow access to services, etc.

**Figure 5.43** Square and splayed heading

The first board is nailed down about 10–12 mm from the wall. The remaining boards can be fixed four to six boards at a time, leaving a 10–12 mm gap around the perimeter to allow for expansion. This gap will eventually be covered by the skirting board.

There are two methods of clamping the boards before fixing:

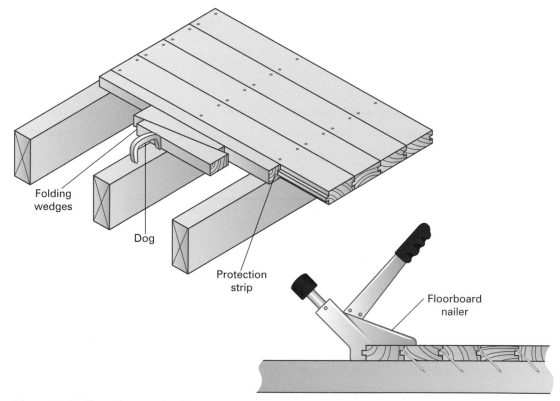

Folding wedges

Dog

Protection strip

Floorboard nailer

**Figure 5.44** Clamping methods

## Chipboard flooring

Flooring-grade chipboard is increasingly being used for domestic floors. It is available in sheet sizes of $2440 \times 600 \times 18$ mm and can be square edged or tongued and grooved on all edges, the latter being preferred. If square-edged chipboard is used it must be supported along every joint.

Tongued and grooved boards are laid end to end, at right angles to the joists. Cross-joints should be staggered and, as with softwood flooring, expansion gaps of 10–12 mm left around the perimeter. The ends must be supported.

When setting out the floor joists, the spacing should be set to avoid any unnecessary wastage. The boards should be glued along all joints and fixed using either 50–65 mm annular ring shank nails or 50–65 mm screws. Access traps must be created in the flooring to allow access to services such as gas and water.

**(a)** Chipboard floor

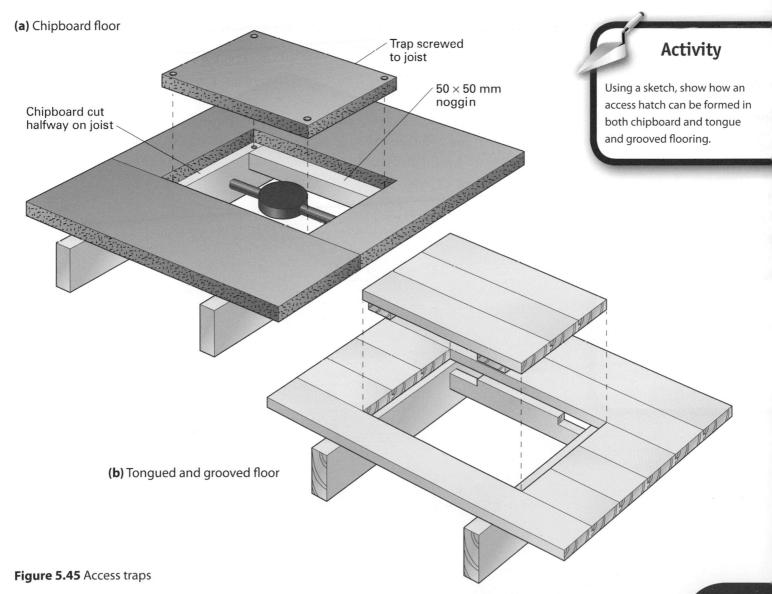

Trap screwed to joist

$50 \times 50$ mm noggin

Chipboard cut halfway on joist

**(b)** Tongued and grooved floor

**Figure 5.45** Access traps

### Activity

Using a sketch, show how an access hatch can be formed in both chipboard and tongue and grooved flooring.

## Solid concrete floors

Solid concrete floors are more durable than suspended timber floors. They are constructed on a sub-base incorporating hardcore, damp proof membranes and insulation. The depth of the hardcore and concrete will depend on the nature of the building, and will be set by the Building Regulations and the local authority.

In the next few pages, you will look at:

- formwork for concrete floors
- reinforcement
- compacting of concrete
- surface finishes
- curing.

Any concreting job has to be supported at the sides to prevent the concrete just running off and this support comes in the way of formwork.

## Formwork for ground floors

Floors for buildings such as factories and warehouses etc. have large areas and would be difficult to lay in one slab. Floors of this type are usually laid in alternative strips up to 4.5 m wide, running the full length of the building (see Figure 5.46). The actual formwork would be similar to that used for paths.

**Activity**

Using a sketch, show how formwork for ground floors can be created.

**Activity**

In an area designated by your trainer, create formwork for concrete flooring.

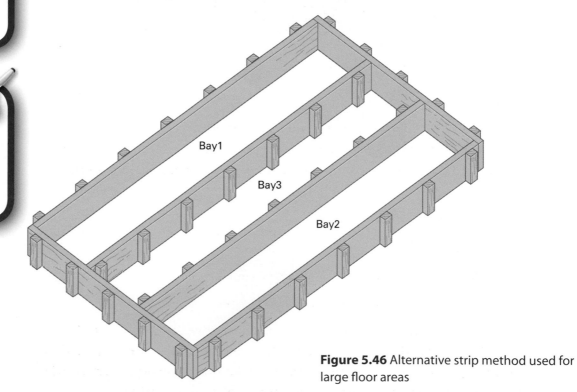

**Figure 5.46** Alternative strip method used for large floor areas

## Reinforcement

Concrete is strong in **compression** but weak in **tension** so, to prevent concrete from being 'pulled' apart when under pressure, steel reinforcement is provided. The type and position of the reinforcement will be specified by the structural engineer.

The reinforcement must always have a suitable thickness of concrete cover to prevent the steel from rusting if exposed to moisture or air. The amount of cover required depends upon the location of the site with respect to exposure conditions, and ranges from 20 mm in mild exposure to 60 mm for very severe exposure to water.

To prevent the reinforcement from touching the formwork, spacers made from concrete, fibre cement or plastic are used. They are available in several shapes and various sizes to give the correct cover.

**Definition**

**Compression** – being squeezed or squashed together

**Tension** – being stretched

Steel reinforcement of concrete

## Compacting

When concrete has been placed, it contains trapped air in the form of voids. To get rid of these voids we must compact the concrete. The more workable the concrete the easier it would be to compact, but also if the concrete is too wet, the excess water will reduce the strength of the concrete.

Failure to compact concrete results in:

- reduction in the strength of the concrete
- water entering the concrete, which could damage the reinforcement
- visual defects, such as honeycombing on the surface.

The method of compaction depends on the thickness and the purpose of the concrete. For oversite concrete, floors and pathways up to 100 mm thick, manual compaction with a tamper board may be sufficient. This requires slightly overfilling the formwork and tamping down with the tamper board. For larger spans the tamper board may be fitted with handles.

Tamper board with handles

For slabs up to 150 mm thick, a vibrating beam tamper should be used. This is simply a tamper board with a petrol-driven vibrating unit bolted on. The beam is laid on the concrete with its motor running and is pulled along the slab.

For deeper structures, such as retaining walls for example, a poker vibrator would be required. The poker vibrator is a vibrating tube at the end of a flexible drive connected to a petrol motor. The pokers are available in various diameters from 25 mm to 75 mm.

The concrete should be laid in layers of 600 mm with the poker in vertically and penetrating the layer below by 100 mm. The concrete is vibrated until the air bubbles stop and the poker is then lifted slowly and placed 150 to 1000 mm from this incision, depending on the diameter of the vibrator.

## Surface finishes

Vibrating beam tamper

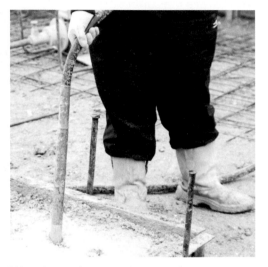
Vibrating poker in use

Surface finishes for slabs may be:

- **Tamped finish.** Simply using a straight edge or tamper board when compacting the concrete will leave a rough finish to the floor, ideal for a path or drive surface, giving grip to vehicles and pedestrians. This finish may also be used if a further layer is to be applied to give a good bond.

- **Float and brush finish.** After **screeding** off the concrete with a straight edge, the surface is floated off using a steel or wooden float and then brushed lightly with a soft brush (see photo opposite). Again, this would be suitable for pathways and drives.

- **Steel float finish.** After screeding off using a straight edge, a steel float is applied to the surface. This finish attracts particles of cement to the surface, causing the concrete to become impermeable to water but also very slippery when wet. This is not very suitable for outside but ideal for use indoors for floors, etc.

- **Power trowelling/float.** Three hours after laying, a power float is applied to the surface of the concrete. After a further delay to allow surface water to evaporate, a power trowel is then used. A power float has a rotating circular disc or four large flat blades powered by a petrol engine. The edges of the blades are turned up to prevent them digging into the concrete slab. This finish would most likely be used in factories where a large floor area would be needed.

- **Power grinding.** This is a technique used to provide a durable wearing surface without further treatment. The concrete is laid, compacted and trowel finished. After 1 to 7 days the floor is ground, removing the top 1–2 mm, leaving a polished concrete surface.

**Definition**

**Screeding** – levelling off concrete by adding a final layer

**Remember**

Make sure you always clean all tampers and tools after use.

Brushed concrete finish

Power float

**Did you know?**

The success of surface finishes depends largely on timing. You need to be aware of the setting times in order to apply the finish.

Surface treatment for other surfaces may be:

- **Plain smooth surfaces.** After the formwork has been struck, the concrete may be polished with a carborundum stone, giving a polished water-resistant finish.

- **Textured and profiled finish.** A simple textured finish may be made by using rough sawn boards to make the formwork. When struck, the concrete takes on the texture of these boards. A profiled finish can be made by using a lining inside the formwork. The linings may be made from polystyrene or flexible rubber-like plastics, and gives a pattern to the finished concrete.

- **Ribbed finish.** These are made by fixing timber battens to the formwork.

Ribbed concrete finish

- **Exposed aggregate finish.** The coarse aggregate is exposed by removing the sand and cement from the finished concrete with a sand blaster. Another method of producing this finish is by applying a chemical retarder to the formwork, which prevents the cement in contact with it from hardening. When the formwork is removed, the mortar is brushed away to uncover the aggregate in the hardened concrete.

## Curing

When concrete is mixed, the quantity of water is accurately added to allow for hydration to take place. The longer we can keep this chemical reaction going, the stronger the concrete will become.

To allow the concrete to achieve its maximum strength, the chemical reaction must be allowed to keep going for as long as possible. To do this we must 'cure' the concrete. This is done by keeping the concrete damp and preventing it from drying out too quickly.

Curing can be done by:

1. Spraying the concrete with a chemical sealer, which dries to leave a film of resin to seal the surface and reduces the loss of moisture.

2. Spraying the concrete with water, which replaces any lost water and keeps the concrete damp. This can also be done by placing sand or hessian cloth or other similar material on the concrete and dampening.

3. Covering the concrete with a plastic sheet or building paper, preventing wind and sun from evaporating the water into the air. Any evaporated moisture due to the heat will condense on the polythene and drip back on to the concrete surface.

## Concreting in hot weather

When concreting in temperatures over 20°C, there is a reduction in workability due to the water being lost through evaporation. The cement also tends to react more quickly with water, causing the concrete to set rapidly.

To remedy the problem of the concrete setting quickly, a 'retarding mixture' may be used. This slows down the initial reaction between the cement and water, allowing the concrete to remain workable for longer.

Extra water may be added at the time of mixing so that the workability would be correct at the time of placing.

Water must *not* be added during the placing of the concrete, to make it more workable, after the initial set has taken place in the concrete.

# Concreting in cold weather

Water expands when freezing. This can cause permanent damage if the concrete is allowed to freeze when freshly laid or in hardened concrete that has not reached enough strength ($5 \text{ N/mm}^2$, which takes 48 hours).

Concreting should not take place when the temperature is 2°C or less. If the temperature is only slightly above 2°C, mixing water should be heated.

After being laid, the concrete should be kept warm by covering with insulating quilts, which allows the cement to continue its reaction with the water and prevents it from freezing.

# Beam and block floors

Construction of these floors is generally quite simple. Unlike solid floor construction, they can be fitted at both ground floor level and upper floor levels.

Depending on site conditions, beam and block floors can be installed in most types of weather and by using a variety of methods including mobile cranes or other site lifting plant or by hand.

Standard beam and block floors consist of 150 mm and 225 mm beams with standard 100 mm deep concrete building blocks inserted between the beams.

The beams are pre-cast away from the site environment and are pre-stressed with high tensile steel wires suited to the environment and purpose for which they are to be used.

Once the blocks have been placed in position, the floor should be grouted with sand / cement grout consisting of four parts sand to one part cement. The grout should be brushed into the joints between the beams and the blocks in order to stabilise the floor.

Insulation can be slung underneath the beams or over the blocks where it is to be covered with a suitable finish.

The illustration shows a typical beam and block floor construction. The air brick is there to ventilate the airspace below the floor.

## Safety tip

The beams in a beam and block floor can be heavy, so you may need a crane to position them on the external walls safely.

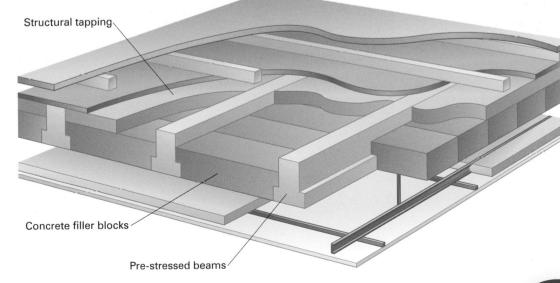

Structural tapping

Concrete filler blocks

Pre-stressed beams

**Figure 5.47** Typical beam and block floor

## Floating floors

These are basic timber floor constructions that are laid on a solid concrete floor. The timbers are laid in a similar way to joists, although they are usually 50 mm thick maximum as there is no need for support. The timbers are laid on the floor at predetermined centres, and are not fixed to the concrete base (hence floating floor); the decking is then fixed on the timbers. Insulation or underfloor heating can be placed between the timbers to enhance the thermal and acoustic properties.

This type of floor 'floats' on a cushion of insulation. Floating floors are normally manufactured from chipboard – either standard or moisture-resistant – for use in bathrooms. This type of floor is ideal for refurbishment work and where insulation upgrading is required.

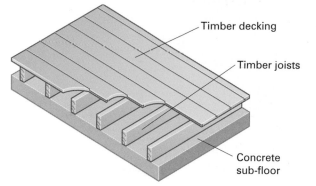

Timber decking

Timber joists

Concrete sub-floor

**Figure 5.48** Floating floor

## Activity

Draw a sketch to show how floating floors are created.

## Knowledge refresher

1 List the four most common types of floor construction.

2 On a suspended timber floor, what is the difference between a single and a double floor?

3 How can the depth of a timber joist be worked out?

4 What is the difference between solid and herringbone strutting?

5 State the purpose of formwork in concrete floors.

6 Why is reinforcement used in solid concrete flooring?

7 Why is concrete compacted?

8 Describe three ways of finishing a concrete floor.

9 Where would a floating floor be laid?

# What would you do?

**!**

1   You have been asked to quote for building a garage. The client is unsure of what type of floor to have. They ask your opinion. What type of floor would you select? Why would you select that type of floor? What could influence your selection?

2   You have been tasked with joisting an upper floor. You fit the herringbone strutting but, when it comes to fitting the floor and plasterboarding the ceiling, the strutting is interfering with both the floor and the ceiling. What could have caused this? What could be done to rectify it?

# Roofing

Although there are several different types of roofing, all roofs will technically be either a flat roof or a pitched roof.

## Flat roofs

A flat roof is any roof which has its upper surface inclined at an angle (also known as the fall, slope or pitch) not exceeding 10 degrees.

A flat roof has a fall to allow rainwater to run off, preventing puddles forming as they can put extra weight on the roof and cause leaks. Flat roofs will eventually leak, so most are guaranteed for only 10 years (every 10 years or so the roof will have to be stripped back and re-covered). Today **fibreglass** flat roofs are available that last much longer, so some companies will give a 25-year guarantee on their roof. Installing a fibreglass roof is a job for specialist roofers.

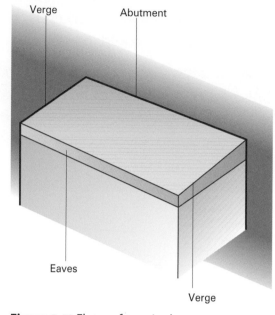

**Figure 5.49** Flat roof terminology

The amount of fall should be sufficient to clear water away to the outlet pipe(s) or guttering as quickly as possible across the whole roof surface. This may involve a single direction of fall or several directional changes of fall such as:

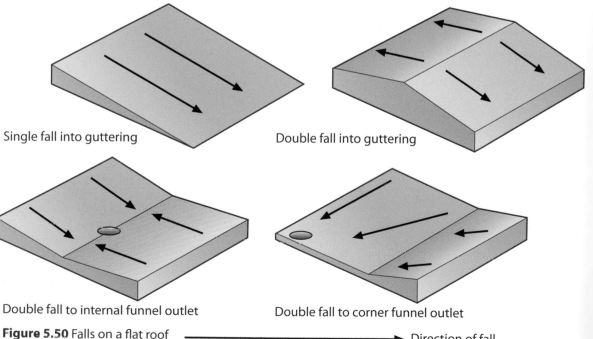

Single fall into guttering

Double fall into guttering

Double fall to internal funnel outlet

Double fall to corner funnel outlet

**Figure 5.50** Falls on a flat roof  Direction of fall

# Pitched roofs

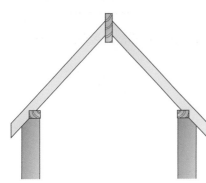

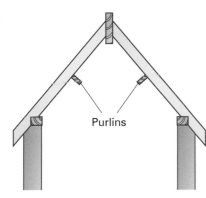

**Figure 5.51** Single roof

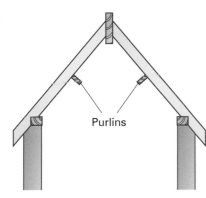

Purlins

**Figure 5.52** Double roof

There are several different types of **pitched roof** but most are constructed in one of two ways.

- **Trussed roof** – A prefabricated pitched roof specially manufactured prior to delivery on site, saving timber as well as making the process easier and quicker. Trussed roofs can also span greater distances without the need for support from intermediate walls.

- **Traditional roof** – A roof entirely constructed on site from loose timber sections using simple jointing methods.

## Roof types

A pitched roof can be constructed either as a single roof, where the rafters do not require any intermediate support, or a double roof where the rafters are supported. Single roofs are used over a short span such as a garage; double roofs are used to span a longer distance such as a house or factory.

There are many different types of pitched roof including:

- **mono pitch** with a single pitch
- **lean-to** with a single pitch, which butts up to an existing building
- **duo pitch** with **gable ends**

> ### Safety tip
>
> Roofing requires working at height so always use the appropriate access equipment (i.e. a scaffold or at least properly secured ladders, trestles or a temporary working platform).

> ### Activity
>
> Use sketches to show the difference between a single roof and a double roof.

**Figure 5.53** Mono pitch roof

**Figure 5.54** Lean-to roof

**Figure 5.55** Duo pitch roof with gable ends

**Figure 5.56** Hipped roof

**Figure 5.57** Over hip roof

**Figure 5.58** Mansard roof

- **hipped roof** with hip ends incorporating crown, hip and jack rafters

- **over hip** with gable ends, hips and valleys incorporating valley and cripple rafters

- **mansard** with gable ends and two different pitches used mainly when the roof space is to be used as a room

- **gable hip** or **gambrel** – double-pitched roof with a small gable (gablet) at the ridge and the lower part a half-hip

- **jerkin-head** or **barn hip** – double-pitched roof hipped from the ridge part-way to the eaves, with the remainder gabled.

The type of roof used will be selected by the client and architect.

## Trussed rafters

Most roofing on domestic dwellings now comprises factory-made trussed rafters. These are made of stress graded, **PAR** timber to a wide variety of designs, depending on requirements. All joints are butt jointed and held together with fixing plates, face fixed on either side. These plates are usually made of galvanised steel and either nailed or factory pressed. They may also be **gang-nailed** gusset plates made of 12 mm resin bonded plywood.

One of the main advantages of this type of roof is the clear span achieved, as there is no need for intermediate, load-bearing partition walls. Standard trusses are strong enough to resist the eventual load of the roofing materials. However, they are not able to withstand pressures applied by lateral bending. Hence, damage is most likely to occur during delivery, movement across site, site storage or lifting into position.

Wall plates are bedded as described above. Following this, the positions of the trusses can be marked at a maximum of 600 mm between centres along each wall plate. The sequence of operations then varies between gable and hipped roofs.

## Definition

**PAR** – a term used for timber that has been 'planed all round'

**Gang-nailed** – galvanised plate with spikes used to secure butt joints

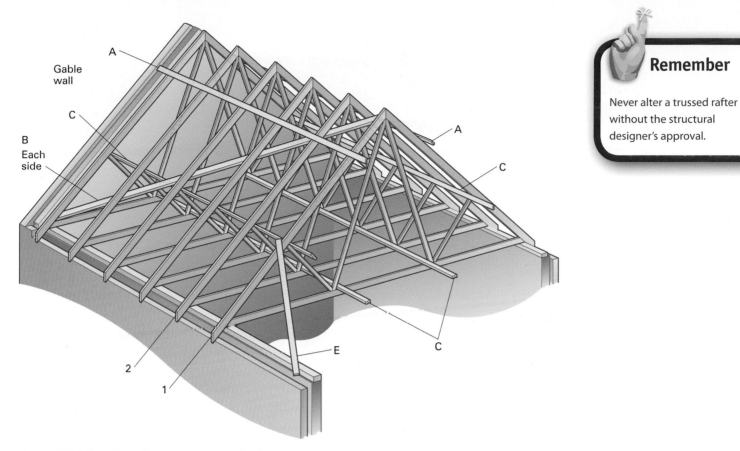

Gable
wall

B
Each
side

**Figure 5.59** Erection of common trussed rafters

## Hipped roofs

In a fully hipped roof there are no gables and the eaves run around the perimeter, so there is no roof ladder or bargeboard.

### Marking out for a hipped roof

All bevels or angles cut on a hipped roof are based on the right-angled triangle and the roof members can be set out using the following two methods:

- **Roofing ready reckoner** – a book that lists in table form all the angles and lengths of the various rafters for any span or rise of roof.

- **Geometry** – working with scale drawings and basic mathematic principles to give you the lengths and angles of all rafters.

The ready reckoner will be looked at later in this chapter, so for now we will concentrate on geometry.

## Pythagoras' theorem

When setting out a hipped roof, you need to know Pythagoras' theorem. Pythagoras states that 'the square on the hypotenuse of a right-angled triangle is equal to the sum of the squares on the other two sides'. For the carpenter, the 'hypotenuse' is the rafter length, while the 'other two sides' are the run and the rise.

From Pythagoras' theorem, we get this calculation:

$A = \sqrt{B^2 + C^2}$ ($\sqrt{}$ means the square root and $^2$ means squared)

If we again look at our right-angled triangle we can break it down to:

A (the rafter length – the distance we want to know)

$B^2$ (the rise, multiplied by itself)

$C^2$ (the run, multiplied by itself).

Therefore, we have all we need to find out the length of our rafter (A):

$A = \sqrt{4^2 + 3^2}$

$A = \sqrt{4 \times 4 + 3 \times 3}$

$A = \sqrt{16 + 9}$

$A = \sqrt{25}$

$A = 5$

so our rafter would be 5 m long.

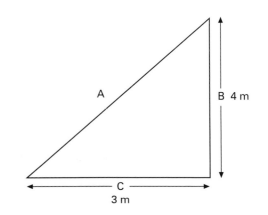

## Finishing a roof at the gable and eaves

There are two types of finish for a gable end:

- a flush finish, where the bargeboard is fixed directly onto the gable wall
- a roof ladder – a frame built to give an overhang and to which the bargeboard and soffit are fixed.

The most common way is to use a roof ladder which, when creating an overhang, stops rainwater running down the face of the gable wall.

The continuation of the fascia board around the verge of the roof is called the bargeboard. Usually the bargeboard is fixed to the roof ladder and has a built-up section at the bottom to encase the wall plate.

The simplest way of marking out the bargeboard is to temporarily fix it in place and use a level to mark the plumb and seat cut.

**Activity**

Use sketches to show how a gable ladder and bargeboard are fitted.

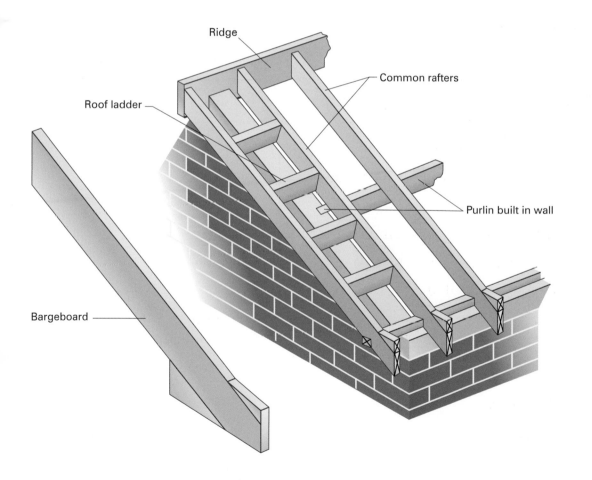

**Figure 5.60** Roof ladder with bargeboard fitted

## *Eaves details*

The eaves are how the lower part of the roof is finished where it meets the wall, and incorporates fascia and soffit. The fascia is the vertical board fixed to the ends of the rafters. It is used to close the eaves and allow fixing for rainwater pipes. The soffit is the horizontal board fixed to the bottom of the rafters and the wall. It is used to close the roof space to prevent birds or insects from nesting there, and usually incorporates ventilation to help prevent rot.

There are various ways of finishing a roof at the eaves; we will look at the four most common.

### Flush eaves

Here the eaves are finished as close to the wall as possible. There is no soffit, but a small gap is left for ventilation.

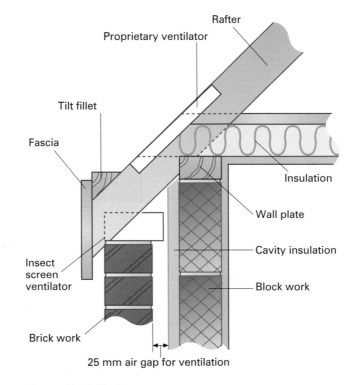

**Figure 5.61** Flush eaves

## Open eaves

An open eaves is where the bottom of the rafter feet are planed as they are exposed. The rafter feet project beyond the outer wall and eaves boards are fitted to the top of the rafters to hide the underside of the roof cladding. The rainwater pipes are fitted via brackets fixed to the rafter ends.

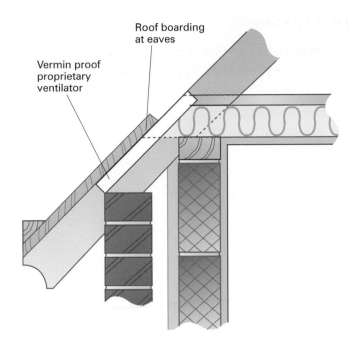

**Figure 5.62** Open eaves

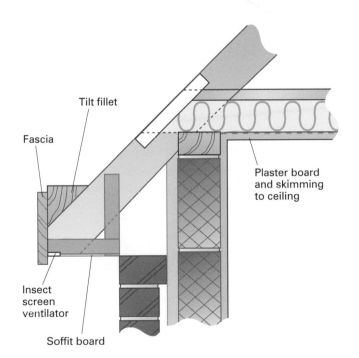

**Figure 5.63** Closed eaves

## Closed eaves

Closed eaves are completely closed or boxed in. The ends of the rafters are cut to allow the fascia and soffit to be fitted. The roof is ventilated either by ventilation strips incorporated into the soffit or by holes drilled into the soffit with insect-proof netting over them. If closed eaves are to be re-clad due to rot you must ensure that the ventilation areas are not covered up.

## Sprocketed eaves

Sprocketed eaves are used where the roof has a sharp pitch. The **sprocket** reduces the pitch at the eaves, slowing down the flow of rainwater and stopping it overshooting the guttering. Sprockets can either be fixed to the top edge of the rafter or bolted onto the side.

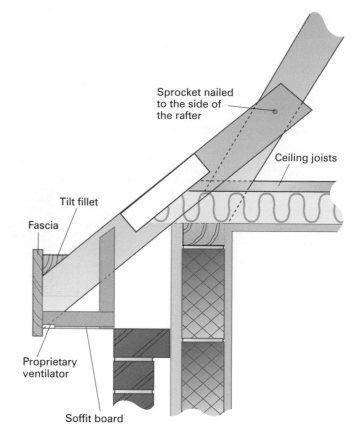

Figure 5.64 Sprocketed eaves

## *Roof coverings*

Once all the rafters are on the roof, the final thing is to cover it. There are two main methods of covering a roof, each using different components. Factors affecting the choice of roof covering include what the local weather is like and what load the roof will have to take.

### Method 1

This method is usually used in the north of the country where the roof may be expected to take additional weight from snow.

1.   Clad the roof surface with a man-made board such as OSB or exterior grade plywood.

2.   Cover the roof with roofing felt starting at the bottom and ensuring the felt is overlapped to stop water getting in.

3.   Fit the felt battens (battens fixed vertically and placed to keep the felt down while allowing ventilation) and the tile battens (battens fixed horizontally and accurately spaced to allow the tiles to be fitted with the correct overlap).

4.   Finally, fit the tiles and cement on the ridge.

## Method 2

This is the most common way of covering a roof.

1.  Fit felt directly onto the rafters.

2.  Fit the tile battens at the correct spacing.

3.  Fit the tiles and cement on the ridge.

Another way to cover a roof involves using slate instead of tiles. Slate-covered roofing is a specialised job as the slates often have to be cut to fit, so roofers usually carry this out.

## Knowledge refresher

1  What is the definition of a flat roof?

2  What is the difference between a truss roof and a cut roof?

3  Explain the difference between a hip and a gable end.

4  What is the purpose of a roof ladder?

5  Describe an 'I' type joist.

## What would you do?

You have been asked to quote for building a garage. The client is unsure about what type of roof to have. They ask your opinion. What type of roof would you select? Why would you select that type of roof? What could influence your selection?

| Element | Domestic | Commercial |
| --- | --- | --- |
| Foundations | Traditional strip footings<br>Raft foundations on poor load-bearing ground<br>Mass-fill trench foundations | Piled foundations with pile caps<br>Ground beams<br>Raft foundations with edge beam<br>Pad foundations |
| Structural frame | Traditional cavity wall<br>Timber-framed construction<br>Load-bearing insulated formwork | Steel portal frame<br>Steel columns and beams<br>Composite construction<br>Concrete frameworks |
| Cladding | Facing brickwork<br>Rendering<br>Timber cladding<br>Clay tiles | Insulated composite cladding panels<br>Steel powder-coated panels<br>Brickwork facing skin dwarf walls<br>Timber cladding |
| Flooring | Solid concrete floors<br>Beam and block<br>Traditional timber flooring joists | Solid reinforced concrete floors, power-floated with edge beams |
| Roofing | Roof trusses with interlocking roof tiles<br>Traditional roof timbering with clay/concrete roof tiles | Insulated cladding panels |

**Table 5.1** Comparison between domestic and commercial construction techniques

# chapter 6

# Energy efficiency and sustainability

## OVERVIEW

Many of us are aware of the growing concerns around global warming and the current focus on minimising our 'carbon footprint'. This chapter deals with some of the factors that may be contributing to climate change, and the way in which modern construction methods and design can help to tackle it by creating a more sustainable environment – an environment that provides for the needs of the present without compromising the needs of future generations.

Energy efficiency and the reduction of wastage are now goals for every building project, and must be considered carefully, from the design stage right through the building process.

In this chapter, you will look at the modern materials and methods used to create structures in an energy-efficient way, with sustainability in mind.

This chapter will cover:

- the impact of climate change

- the role of the construction industry in tackling climate change

- sustainable construction methods

- environmental design considerations

- insulation

- how sustainability affects the different elements of a structure

- the energy efficiency and sustainability of different materials and components

- making materials last longer.

# Climate change

Although much controversy surrounds climate change, it is hard to ignore the changes in weather patterns that we have witnessed recently, not just in the UK but also around the world. In the UK, these changes have resulted in extensive flooding, with winter months becoming warmer and summer months becoming wetter. Around the world, the ice caps are melting at worrying speeds, sea levels are rising and adverse weather systems have resulted in more frequent tornados and tropical storms.

The changing climate will certainly impact on the way we design buildings in order to cope with some of the possible effects, which include:

- rising temperatures
- rising sea levels
- rising amounts of rainfall
- higher humidity levels.

Area of land under flood

Although not fully proven, a number of factors are thought to contribute to global warming. The main causes are considered to be burning fossil fuels and the high levels of $CO_2$ being emitted into the air. $CO_2$ is emitted in many different ways including through car emissions, aerosol gases and burning untreated waste products.

Many practices have been introduced in an attempt to reduce the carbon footprint, and many more initiatives are being planned, including:

- recycling of packaging such as plastics, paper, cardboard, metals and glass
- use of alternative fuels to power cars and industrial machinery
- use of natural resources such as wind to supply electricity
- transport sharing to reduce the number of cars on the road, thus reducing $CO_2$ emissions.

## Definition

**Carbon footprint** – total amount of $CO_2$ emissions produced by individuals and industry

New legislation has been introduced to make sure that the industry works towards the design of energy-efficient buildings, but at the same time the construction industry is becoming more conscious of the need to address climate change itself, by introducing its own initiatives and practices to minimise its carbon footprint.

**Find out**

Identify other initiatives and practices currently being used or developed in an attempt to reduce people's carbon footprint.

- The construction industry is putting greater emphasis on reducing building waste, and is being proactive in recycling many materials that would once have been disposed of to the detriment of the environment.

- There have been significant changes in the design of both domestic and industrial buildings.

- More natural resources are being used in the construction of buildings which, when the building is demolished, can be reused on a new development.

- Buildings now have improved insulation properties, thus reducing fuel usage for heating.

- There are alternative methods of providing energy for a building, including the use of solar panels to provide natural heat.

There are many, many ways of making buildings eco-friendly and we will look at some of these later in this chapter.

# Sustainable construction methods

Modern construction methods have been developed in response to the new legislation on sustainability.

## Cavity walling

Thirty years ago, it was quite acceptable to build a cavity 75 to 85 mm wide that had very little insulation included in its construction. Modern methods of cavity wall construction now allow for a cavity that is 100 mm wide and is fully filled with glass fibre cavity wall batt insulation, with an engineered lightweight internal skin of blockwork. In Chapter 5, you saw how spaced stainless steel wall ties are used to provide structural integrity to the completed wall, and how the insulation is not clipped.

In commercial buildings, cavity walls tend to be used in the bottom storey, while portal-framed construction with insulated cladding is usually used for the upper half of the unit.

Solar panels on a domestic dwelling

# Timber-framed construction

Timber-framed construction is a fast, easy and efficient method of producing domestic buildings, and is sustainable in its approach as it uses timber from managed forests.

With timber-framed construction, the insulation is placed internally between the studs and covered with a DPM and plasterboard. A traditional skin of brickwork clads the exterior, and a cavity can be formed by covering the plywood panels with a breathable membrane. Stainless steel ties are screwed to the plywood to provide support for the brickwork.

The floors and roof are traditionally constructed, but the timber-framed panels can be prefabricated off site, which can have its own implications for energy efficiency.

## Alternative construction methods

A number of other energy-efficient construction methods are growing in popularity.

### *Insulated concrete formwork*

This is the 'Lego brick' construction method where hollow, moulded polystyrene forms are literally snapped together to form a wall, with the help of locating **castellations** on each form. Reinforcing rods are added where required and concrete is poured into the moulds and allowed to set. A solid wall is formed that can be rendered externally and plastered internally. Traditional brick cladding can be used externally to clad the structure.

Insulated concrete formwork is faster and more energy-efficient than more traditional construction methods as it uses less concrete, saves on site resources (for example, no bricklayers are needed), and the insulation is included as part of the formwork. Once constructed, the formwork can simply be rendered and plastered.

Energy-efficient insulated formwork

## Insulated panel construction

This is a system that uses insulation bonded to the plywood panels that form a structural wall. Traditional cladding – both external and internal – can then be used to cover the insulated panel frames, using the same process as with the timber-framed construction.

This construction method uses pre-formed factory panels that can be readily assembled on site, saving time and resources, and finishing trades can come in earlier than usual, while the outer skin is being completed. The insulated panels are also highly thermally efficient.

## Thin joint masonry

This is a system that uses high-quality dimensioned blocks that are up to three times the size of normal blocks. A cement-based adhesive is used to bond the locks together using 1 mm tight joints. The starting base course of brickwork has to be very accurate in its setting out and level. Traditional cavities are formed using helix type wall ties that are just driven into the thin joint masonry using a hammer.

This uses lightweight, thermally efficient blocks with no mortar, so it is faster and cheaper to construct, there is less waste, and the end product is very energy efficient.

# Environmental design considerations

The design of a building or structure should now take on elements that make it environmentally friendly, both in its construction and in the way the occupants use it. The design should also take into account the needs of the local community, in terms of the infrastructure that will be needed to support its eventual construction and use.

Environmental considerations may include some or all of these elements.

- **The design brief** – This should aim to create a design that lowers pollutants to the atmosphere, reduces waste in its construction, reduces noise pollution, and gives the local community something that it can enjoy.

- **Recycling materials** – The design should specify the inclusion of recycled materials into the structure and aesthetics of the building project: for example, the use of crushed hardcore from demolition on site, or the reuse of slate roofing materials.

- **Energy efficiency** – The amount of **embedded** and used energy must be carefully considered for each element of the design, from boiler management systems to highly engineered aerated concrete thermal blocks.

- **Sustainability** – The design must contain elements that will meet the needs of future generations. A long, maintenance-free life span for the building is essential. Spending more at the initial cost stage can pay dividends in the future by reducing the cost of energy use and maintenance later on.

## Activity

There are several major block manufacturers which produce the thin joint masonry system. Find one of their websites and produce a short presentation that includes:

- the advantages and benefits of the system
- why this system is sustainable
- a photograph showing how the blocks are joined.

## Definition

**Embedded energy** – the amount of energy that has been used to create and manufacture the material and transport it to site for inclusion in the structure

- **Green materials** – The use of green materials is a vital environmentally friendly way of ensuring minimum impact on the local and global environment. For example, cedar timber boarding is a sustainable timber product that does not require chemical treatment or painting.

## Knowledge refresher

1 Your client is considering moving away from traditional brick cavity walls to produce domestic dwellings. You have been asked to provide details of two alternative methods. Name two alternative modern construction methods that could be used.

2 Thin joint masonry does not use mortar to bond the blocks together. What product does it use?

3 What is the width of the cavity in timber-framed construction?

4 How is insulated concrete formwork finished externally?

5 What size is a modern cavity width in millimetres?

## Insulation

The term 'building insulation' refers broadly to any object in a building used as insulation for any purposes – the term applies to both acoustic insulation and fire insulation as well as thermal insulation. Often an insulation material will be chosen for its ability to perform several of these functions at once.

Insulating buildings is vital: maintaining acceptable temperature in buildings (by heating or cooling) uses a large proportion of a building's total energy consumption, and the insulation can help to reduce this energy use.

The effectiveness of insulation is commonly related to its **R-value**. However, the R-value does not take into account the quality of construction or local environmental factors for each building. Construction quality issues include poor vapour barrier and problems with draught-proofing. Local environmental factors are simply about where the building is located. With cold climates, the main aim is to reduce heat flow from the building; with hot climates, the main aim is to reduce the heat from entering the building, usually through solar radiation, which can enter a building through the windows.

## Materials used in insulating homes

There are essentially two types of building insulation: bulk insulation and reflective insulation.

- **Bulk insulation** – this blocks conductive heat transfer and convective flow, either into or out of a building. The denser the material is, the better it will conduct heat. As air has such a low density, it is a very poor conductor – and therefore a good insulator. This is why air trapped between two materials is often used as an insulator, as in cavity walling.

- **Reflective insulation** – this works by creating a radiant heat barrier in conjunction with an air space, to reduce the heat transfer across the air space. Reflective insulation reflects heat rather than absorbing it or letting it pass through. It is often seen in the form of reflective pads placed behind radiators to reflect the heat from the rear of the radiator back into the room.

## Forms of insulation

There are various forms of insulation, but the most common are:

- **mineral wool/rock wool** – these products are made from molten rock spun on a high-spinning machine at a temperature of about 1600°C, similar to the process of making candy floss, with the product being a mass of fine, intertwined fibres

- **fibreglass** – made in a similar way to rock wool, but using molten glass.

Mineral wool usually comes in sheets that are cut to fit between the rafters or studs. Fibreglass is similar, although it can come in rolls that can be cut to fit. Both materials are available in a variety of thicknesses to suit where they are going to be laid.

Other forms of insulation include:

- **polystyrene sheet**s – polystyrene is a thermoplastic substance that comes in sheets which can be cut to size, again available in different thicknesses

- **loose-fill insulation** – this is particularly used where there is no insulation in the cavity walls: holes are drilled in the exterior wall and glass wool insulation is blown into the holes until the cavity is full.

### *Where to insulate*

Where insulation should be used depends on the climate and the particular living needs, but generally insulation should be placed:

- in the roof space, between rafters or trusses and between joists

- on all exterior walls

- between the joists at every floor level, including ground floor

- in solid ground floor construction
- in partition walls
- around any ducts and pipes.

In the next section, you will see how insulation techniques can be applied to the different elements of a structure.

# How sustainability affects the different elements of a structure

## The sub-structure

Foundations need to be accurately set out to prevent wastage of materials: for example, the concrete in the foundations.

Cement manufacture is one of the processes that uses a high amount of energy and produces high carbon emissions. For example, by making a foundation larger than you require – perhaps because of an overdig by the excavator – you are using more material than you need to. As well as costing the client more, this will waste energy.

Sustainable excavation involves not removing the excavated material from the site. Removing excavated material incurs tip charges, which are part of the landfill tax. Dumping of waste into the land is now not a cheap option. By forming landscaped mounds on site, which can be planted and made into attractive green areas, you can increase the environmentally friendly impact of the excavation and save valuable resources in several ways, including reduced fuel charges, transport costs, air pollution and taxation.

## Find out

Find out more about the landfill tax, on the internet or at your local library.

The depth to which foundations have to be taken is governed by Building Control Inspection

The depth to which foundations have to be taken is governed by Building Control inspection. However, optical and levelling equipment such as profile boards and a traveller must be used to make sure the foundation depth is set out accurately, which will reduce wastage and hence energy use.

Generally, the deeper the foundation, the more expensive and more energy-consuming it is to produce. Deep strip and wide strip are expensive, and it could be better to use piled/ground beam foundations and raft foundations. These foundation types do not require deep, wasteful excavations on site. The soil report and site conditions will need careful consideration at the design stage to produce an energy-efficient design that supports the building's loads safely.

## What would you do? !

Your client is adamant that all excavated materials are to be removed from site. There is a large, open space at the rear of the development. How would you convince the client of the benefits of leaving and landscaping the excavated material on site?

## External walls

### Cavity walls

Cavity walls have been used for the past 60 years. They rely on the external brick skin to keep the impact of the weather elements from crossing the cavity. The inner leaf of blockwork

Blockwork, brick and insulation used in cavity wall construction

is now thermally engineered to trap as much air into its structure as possible, making it lightweight and easy to handle. Openings in cavity walls must be fitted into the construction properly to maximise their energy efficiency.

# Insulation in cavity walls

Cavity walls are insulated mainly to prevent heat loss and therefore save energy. The *Building Regulations* tell us how much insulation is required in various situations, and in most cases this would be stipulated in the specification for the relevant project to obtain planning permission from the local council.

Cavity insulation can be either Rockwall or polystyrene beads.

There are three main ways to insulate the cavity:

1. total or full fill
2. partial fill
3. injection (after construction)

## Total or full fill

Figure 6.1 shows a section of a total fill cavity wall. The cavity is completely filled with insulation 'batts' as the work proceeds. The batts are 450 mm × 1200 mm, are made of mineral fibres, and placed between the horizontal wall ties.

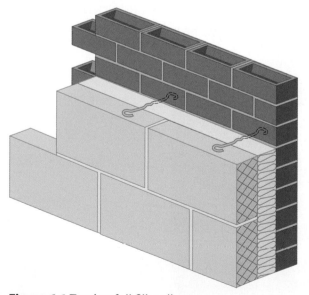

**Figure 6.1** Total or full fill wall

## Partial fill

Figure 6.2 shows a partial filled cavity, where the cavity insulation batts are positioned against the inner leaf and held in place by a plastic clip. More wall ties than usual are used to secure the insulation in place.

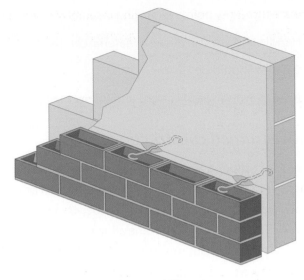

**Figure 6.2** Wall with partial fill cavity

## Injection

This is where the insulation is injected into the cavity after the main structure of the building is complete. Holes are drilled into the inner walls at about 1 m centres and the insulation is pumped into the cavity. The two main materials used are Rockwool fibreglass or polystyrene granules. The holes are then filled with mortar. If an older property were injected, then the holes would be drilled into the external mortar joints.

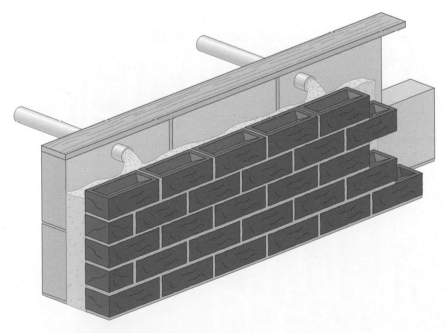

**Figure 6.3** Wall being injected

There are three key points regarding insulating cavity walls:

1. Handle and store insulation material carefully to avoid damage or puncturing.

2. Cavities should be clean.

3. Read drawing specifications and follow manufacturers' instructions carefully.

## Timber-framed construction

This type of timber-frame construction is a recent method of construction, and is highly efficient at preventing heat loss. In timber-framed construction, the traditional internal skin of block work has been replaced by timber-framed panels, which support the load of the structure. The breather membrane allows the passage of vapour in one direction so that the timber can 'breathe', but moisture is not allowed back in – the internal vapour barrier does not allow moisture to pass into the plasterboard.

The insulation within timber-framed construction is kept 'warm' by being placed within the warm side of the construction. It is protected by the vapour barrier and breather membrane.

The outside skin of a timber-framed building can be clad in several different materials, from a traditional brick skin of facing brickwork to rendered blockwork, which is painted.

Timber-framed construction

## Solid walls

Occasionally, during refurbishment work, you may come upon an existing wall that is of solid construction. This tends to be in older houses from the 1890s, where solid brick walls were laid in English bond, with alternate courses of headers and stretchers. This method of construction did not contain a cavity or any insulation, and as such is not very thermally efficient.

Walls for modern-day uninhabited rooms – for example, an outbuilding – can be solid-block walls that are rendered externally to prevent water getting in.

### Remember

Solid walls have to have high-quality brickwork and bonding with full mortar joints in order to prevent moisture getting in.

## What would you do?

You are working on the first phase of a new housing complex. The construction type will be timber-framed, with a brick outer skin. You have started the first course above DPC and the general foreman has told you to place the insulation between the breather membrane and the brick skin. You are not happy about this. What might happen if you do what the foreman says? What should you do?

| Material | Reasons for use |
| --- | --- |
| **Bricks** | Bricks are hardwearing, with a low porosity<br>Available in a wide range of attractive colours and textures, which enhances aesthetics<br>Can be used with coloured mortars to good effect<br>Excellent lifespan |
| **Blocks** | Thermally efficient<br>Lightweight<br>Pre-textured ready to receive wet finishes<br>High dimensional quality |
| **Insulation** | Essential to meet Part L of Building Regulations<br>Sits within cavity – does not need clips if fully filled<br>Thermally efficient component<br>Relative low cost |
| **Wall ties** | Constructed of stainless steel so they do not corrode over time<br>Resist lateral forces on the wall<br>Increase the width of the cavity wall making it more stable |
| **Timber frames** | Lightweight construction method<br>Very fast to construct<br>Thermally efficient<br>Sustainable construction material |
| **Sheathing plywood** | Used to provide strength to the timber frames<br>External quality to resist moisture<br>Strong material in shear<br>Suitable to fix brick ties to |
| **Breather membrane** | Enables the passage of moisture<br>Acts as a weather protector during construction<br>Can be stapled to plywood easily |
| **Vapour barrier** | Prevents the passage of moisture, keeping the internal plasterboard dry<br>Can be stapled to timber studs easily<br>Retains the insulation in place |
| **Plasterboard** | Protects the DPM underneath<br>Final finish to timber stud construction<br>Fire-resistant material |

**Remember**

Cost is just one of the factors that will affect the choice of a material.

**Table 6.1** Reasons for using different materials in external walling

CRAVEN COLLEGE

## Comparison of insulation properties between cavity and timber-framed constructions

### Existing cavity wall

A house that is over 50 years old will have been built with the level of insulation that was required at that time under legislation – which may mean none at all within the cavity wall. The insulation properties of the existing wall can be upgraded in three ways.

- The first is to use a foaming insulation, which is pumped in from the outside. You must take care with any gases that the insulation may give off.

- The second method is to use a blown glass fibre insulation, which is 'blown' under pressure through holes formed in the external brickwork to fill the cavity.

- The final method is to clad the internal walls with either insulation-backed plasterboard attached by dot and dab or timber battens clad in plasterboard. This method does reduce the internal dimensions of the room.

### New cavity construction

This construction is much more thermally efficient, as you can look at reducing heat loss through the structure as a whole. Highly efficient internal blocks are used to form the internal skin, with a 100 mm cavity, which is fully filled using a mineral wool insulation material. The traditional brickwork skin is the same as for the older type of construction – this has not changed over the years.

Modern sheet insulation materials can also be used within cavity construction. Manufactured from high-performance rigid urethane, these materials use space age technology to resist the passage of heat, but may require clipping within a cavity to the wall ties. Therefore, the cavity is said to be partially filled, rather than fully filled.

### Timber-framed construction

This is the most thermally efficient system. It uses insulation (usually quilted) fixed within the timber studs.

Again, rigid insulation products can be used to fill between the timber studs. You can increase the level of insulation by making the timber studs deeper in a mineral wall, or doubling up on rigid insulation boards.

Rigid insulation is normally covered with a foil surface that resists the passage of vapour and slows down the resistance of heat, reflecting it back towards the warm side of the construction.

**Remember**

Any insulation that is retro-fitted is normally put in by a specialist contractor after a building survey.

**Find out**

Find a rigid insulation manufacturer's details for a wall insulation board, and have a look at the fixing details.

**Activity**

To give a visual comparison between cavity and timber-framed construction, produce a sketch drawing of a cross-section through a wall, clearly illustrating the position of the insulation within the construction. Do this for either rigid or quilt insulation materials.

## Internal walls

Internal walls can either be **load-bearing** or non load-bearing. If they are load-bearing, they must be made of materials that can resist the load. In this section, you will investigate the sustainability and energy efficiency of the internal walls and linings most often used in modern construction.

### Fair-faced blockwork

This is economical in terms of the energy used to produce the desired finish: the blockwork produces the completed finish itself, and no secondary wet or dry finishes (plastering or plasterboard) are applied. If the wall is not to be painted, a good quality block must be chosen; if it is to be painted, paint-grade blocks are needed. You must consider the joints between blocks carefully when looking at the type of pointing required. This must be neat and applied to both sides of the wall.

Fair-faced concrete blockwork is an ideal solution for heavily trafficked areas, sports halls and other walls that need a hardwearing surface. However, it may take several coats of paint to produce an acceptable finish on the blockwork surfaces.

### Timber stud walls

A traditional timber stud wall construction

These are constructed using regulated timber studs of equal widths. These are attached to head and sole plates, at the top and floor level respectively. Noggins are added to aid stability and fixing of finishes.

Timber studs are a sustainable timber product. Putting up a timber stud wall is an efficient process, as the walls do not have to dry out and no scaffolding is needed. The studs are normally clad with a plasterboard skin on each side, which can be dry-lined or skim-plastered. With this type of wall, it is also quick and easy to distribute services around a building.

## Metal stud walls

In this system, timber studs are replaced by preformed metal channels. These are fixed together by crimping (using a special tool) or screwing. Metal studs are made with recycled steel, but do have to go through a galvanising process. However, their strength-to-weight ratio is better than timber. Plasterboard finishes are normally screwed into the studs using dry wall screws and a hand-held drill.

Both timber studs and steel channels can be recycled after final use.

## What would you do?

The architect is unsure which of the three systems to incorporate into the ground floor internal layout design. You have been asked to discuss the fixing side of the three methods. Prepare a few notes so that you can discuss these issues with your tutor, who will act as the architect.

## Dry lining

This is the process that lines a surface – normally blockwork – with a plasterboard finish.

'Dot and dab' is a dry lining process. Plasterboard adhesive is applied in dabs to the surface of the wall, and plasterboard is pressed onto the adhesive dabs, then knocked until vertical and aligned with the wall, using a straight edge. A temporary fixing is often used to hold the board in place, and then removed once set. The joints of the plasterboard are bevelled so that a jointing finish tape and filler can be applied to complete the wall.

This process leaves an air gap behind the board, which makes the wall more energy-efficient in terms of heat loss. This dry lining process is useful in refurbishment work, where untidy walls can be easily covered up and upgraded to a quality finish, saving the need to replace whole walls.

## Plastered blockwork

This is the least energy-efficient process because the finish has to dry out, using dehumidifiers and a heat source if necessary (for example, in winter). Wet plaster cannot be painted. A plaster coat is normally applied in two layers, the second being a trowelled and polished final finish that produces a smooth wall. There are various types of plasters to suit the surface the plaster is being applied to and the level of wear the wall will be subjected to.

**Find out**

British Gypsum and Knauf are the UK's leading plaster suppliers. Have a look at their websites and investigate the different types of plaster they manufacture. Can you find any information about sustainability on their websites?

| Material | Reasons for use |
|---|---|
| Fair-faced blockwork | • Economical single process<br>• Can be left as a self-finish<br>• High-quality block available<br>• Saves on secondary resources and energy<br>• Greater sound resistance |
| Timber stud walls | • No wet construction<br>• No drying-out time<br>• Renewable resource<br>• Lightweight construction<br>• Traps air within void that can be insulated<br>• Easy hiding of services |
| Metal stud walls | • Can incorporate recycled steel into manufacture<br>• Good weight-to-strength ratio<br>• Screwed physical fixing of linings<br>• Internal void can be insulated |
| Dry lining | • Covers up untidy backgrounds<br>• Forms air void behind<br>• Can be used with insulation bonded to plasterboard<br>• Quick, easy method of providing a smooth finish<br>• Does not use wet trades<br>• No drying out period |
| Plastered blockwork | • Traditional finish<br>• Hardwearing<br>• Easy to repair |

**Table 6.2** Reasons for using energy-saving materials in internal wall construction

**Remember**

Many factors will affect the choice of a material; fashion is just one.

# Flooring

## Solid floors

Concrete floors are constructed like this.

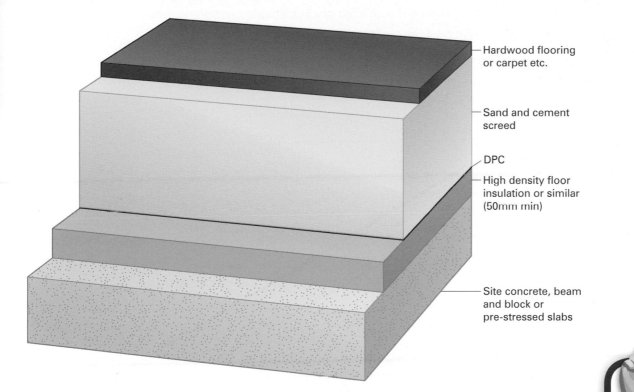

- Hardwood flooring or carpet etc.
- Sand and cement screed
- DPC
- High density floor insulation or similar (50mm min)
- Site concrete, beam and block or pre-stressed slabs

**Figure 6.4** Solid floor construction

The insulation can be placed under or over the concrete, and must be of the right specification to take the loadings from the floor.

## Hollow floors

Beam and block floors require specialist thermal insulation that clips under the beams, below the level of the blocks.

# Roofing

A roof serves several functions: it protects the building from the elements, directs water into gutters and makes the building look aesthetically pleasing. A roof must also meet the requirements of Part L of the Building Regulations, which detail the levels of insulation that must be included to achieve the required **U-value.**

Waterproofing, ventilation and insulation are crucial in making a roof efficient and long lasting, and contribute to the energy efficiency and sustainability of the whole structure.

**Remember**

The insulation manufacturer will be able to help you with typical installation details for placing the thermal insulation into a design.

**Definition**

**U-value** – a measure of thermal transmittance through a building component, usually a roof, wall, window, door or floor

## Pitched roofs

You will remember from Chapter 5 that a pitched roof is made up as follows:

- Softwood rafters span from the ridge to the eaves and are fixed to a wall plate, which is strapped to the internal skin of the wall.

- The rafters are then covered with a felt or a breathable membrane, which stops moisture entering the building if the roof tiles are weakened.

- The felt or membrane is held in place with tile battens manufactured from treated softwood, which are fixed to the rafters using galvanised nails.

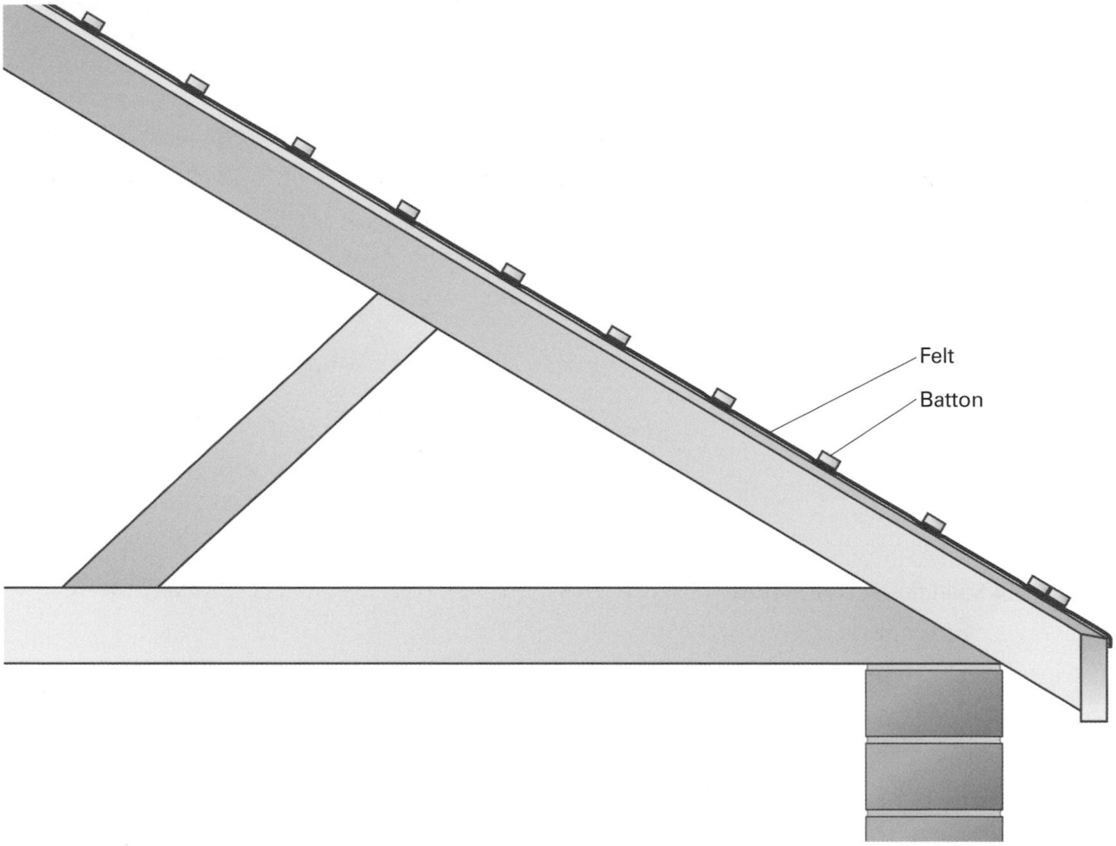

Felt

Batton

**Figure 6.5** Cross-section of a pitched roof showing positioning of felt and battens.

## Insulation

The insulation can be placed in two locations:

- between and over ceiling joists – up to 300 mm of mineral wool insulation (manufactured from glass or rock) is laid, 150 mm between the joists and 150 mm at 90° to this, to form the full thickness

- between or over rafters – form insulation boards are cut and fitted between roof timbers or, with a loft conversion, are laid over the joists before the tile battens and tiling are fitted.

## Waterproofing, damp proofing and ventilation

The ridge is where the two rafters meet at the top of the roof. A fascia and soffit complete the eaves detail of the roof and make it waterproof. Ventilation is provided to prevent the air stagnating, which could lead to the roof timbers rotting. Ventilation may be provided to the roof by placing vents into the soffit or on top of the fascia. In this case, insulation is placed in two layers: one between the ceiling joists, and the other perpendicular to the first layer.

Valleys are formed where two roofs meet within an internal corner. Here a valley board is formed using plywood, which is covered with a flashing to stop water entering. All roof abutments, such as chimneys, must have flashings placed around them to make sure that water cannot get in, causing problems with damp and rot.

## Roof tiles

Roof tiles tend to be chosen to fit in with the local environment, and are often made of local materials: for example, slate in Wales. Most modern roof tiles are manufactured from concrete and have an interlocking system to stop water getting into the roof space.

## Guttering

With both pitched and flat roofs (see below), guttering must be fixed to the fascia board laid to falls, so that rainwater can be directed to fall pipes. The fall pipes connect the guttering to the surface water drainage system. Modern guttering is manufactured from uPVC or aluminum.

## Flat roofs

Flat roofs have notoriously short life spans due to the low pitch and the continual heating and cooling cycle of the environment.

- Normally, felt manufactured with bitumen is used to cover a plywood decking and is laid in three layers, each bonded with bitumen.

- Falls are produced by nailing timber firrings to the roof joists.

- Finally, the roof is covered with a layer of white spar chippings, which reflect the sunlight and prevent solar heat gain from damaging the roof.

With flat roofs, the insulation is set between the joists within the ceiling void or as cut-to-falls insulation, which is laid over the plywood decking and covered with roofing felt. Both methods need a vapour barrier to be fitted, to resist the passage of moisture.

Asphalt is a naturally occurring product. When it is heated up to melting point it can be laid in a single layer onto the prepared roof, forming a single, impenetrable barrier.

**Did you know?**

In the past, guttering used to be manufactured from timber or cast iron.

## Other elements of the structure

### *Insulating timber partitions/floors/roofs*

Insulating between timbers – whether joists or studs – is simply a matter of placing either glass/rock wool or polystyrene between the timbers, with thicker insulation placed between joist roof spaces.

Insulation being fitted between timber

**Figure 6.6** Insulating pipework using mineral wool.

### *Insulating water tanks and pipes*

All water pipes in a loft space or on exterior walls must be insulated to protect them from freezing, which may cause them to crack. There are two methods used when insulating pipes: mineral wool matting or pre-formed moulded insulation.

- **Mineral wool mat** – a small mat is wrapped around the pipes with a bandage and secured with tape or string. The pipes must be completely covered with no gaps, and taps and stopcocks must also be covered.

- **Pre-formed moulded insulation** – this is available to suit different sizes of pipe, and specially formed sections are available for taps and stopcocks. The mouldings can be cut at any angle to fit around bends and when installed the sections of insulation should be taped together to ensure that they are fully enclosed around the pipes and are tightly butted up to one another.

## Insulating water tanks

Any water tanks in the loft space should be insulated around the sides and on the top. The insulation around the sides must extend down to the insulation on the floor of the loft. Insulation jackets are available to fit most sizes and styles of tank.

**Figure 6.7** Use of pre-formed mouldings to insulate pipework.

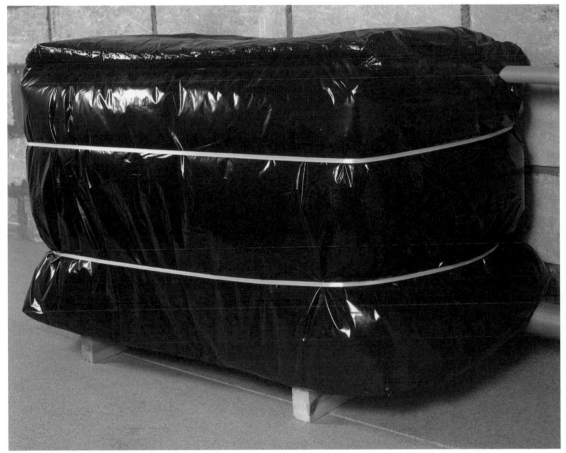

Insulation jacket used to protect water tanks against freezing

### Preventing heat loss in windows and doors

A specialist **FENSA** installer should be used to supply and fit new uPVC windows and doors. These will meet the agreed insulation standard set by the Building Regulations. The cavity should be closed using a thermal bridging product that insulates across the cavity and acts as a DPM, if required.

## Knowledge refresher

1 How is the effectiveness of insulation measured?

2 What is the main reason for using insulation?

3 Describe the two main types of insulation.

4 How is mineral wool formed?

5 List four areas that require insulation.

6 Why should pipes be insulated?

## What would you do?

You have been tasked with insulating a loft space. What type of insulation would you use? Why would you use that type? (Consider cost, workability, R-rating, etc.)

# The energy efficiency and sustainability of different materials and components

## How sustainable are the most common building materials?

As you work in the construction industry, you will come across a vast range of materials. But which of these are the most sustainable? The table below gives a quick overview of the most common building materials, looking at how they are made and any issues to do with their use and disposal.

**Remember**

Sustainability means meeting the needs of future generations, without depleting **finite** resources.

**Definition**

**Finite** – a resource that can never be replaced once used

| Materials | Sustainability |
|---|---|
| Polystyrene | • Petroleum-based product<br>• Can be recycled<br>• Pollution caused through manufacture<br>• Often used as packaging for equipment<br>• High insulation properties |
| Polyurethane | • Made from volatile organic compounds that damage the environment<br>• Often turned into foams<br>• Gives off harmful chemicals if burned<br>• Disposal issues: if the foam catches fire, it causes pollution and produces carcinogenic gases |
| Softwood | • Can be recycled into other products<br>• A managed resource that can be grown over and over again<br>• Provides a pollution filter, takes in carbon dioxide gives out oxygen<br>• A natural 'green' product<br>• Requires treatment to prevent rot |
| Hardwood | • Forms part of the tropical rainforest<br>• Intensively felled<br>• Takes a longer time to re-grow than softwood<br>• Expensive resource |
| Concrete | • Cement production causes $CO_2$ emissions<br>• Disposal issues – can only be crushed and used as hardcore<br>• Hardwearing with a long lifespan<br>• Relies on a lot of formwork and falsework |
| Common brick | • Manufacture involves clay extraction, which has environmental issues<br>• Waste areas form ponds<br>• Uses finite gas energy to fire bricks |

**Table 6.3** Sustainability of common materials

| Materials | Sustainability |
|---|---|
| Facing brick | • Secondary process to produce the patterns and colours<br>• Useful life of up to 100 years<br>• Uses natural products |
| Engineering brick | • Hardwearing, with a long lifespan<br>• Water resistant<br>• Heavy to transport to site, so fuel costs increase |
| Aggregates | • Extracted from gravel pits, causing environmental damage<br>• After extraction, water fills pits to produce another habitat |
| Glass fibre quilt | • Can use recycled glass in manufacture<br>• High insulation value and long lifespan<br>• High thermal insulation-to-weight ratio<br>• Economical transport from factory to site |
| Mineral wool | • Manufactured from glass or rock<br>• Provides a lightweight, high insulation product<br>• Can be used in walls and roof spaces<br>• Can use recycled glass |
| Plasterboard and plaster | • Disposal issues, creating landfill with high sulphate content<br>• High wastage with cutting to size<br>• Manufacture uses gypsum, a waste by-product<br>• Recycling skip agreements in place with manufacturers |
| Concrete block | • Uses cement<br>• Can incorporate waste products from power stations<br>• Sustainable manufacturing process<br>• Take-back recycling schemes for waste blocks |
| Thermal block | • High thermal efficiency<br>• Low weight-to-strength ratio<br>• Uses cement in manufacture additives to produce a block full of air bubbles |
| Metals | • Can use recycled scrap steel in manufacture<br>• Requires secondary treatment to prevent rust<br>• Non-ferrous metals have a long lifespan |
| Glass | • Can be completely recycled<br>• Waste from cutting can be recycled<br>• Issues with recycling: toughened glass has been heat treated as a secondary process, so needs special recycling techniques |

**Table 6.3** (cont.) Sustainability of common materials

# Using sustainable materials

The following materials are the most sustainable of those listed in Table 6.3. You will now take a closer look at their use in domestic and commercial dwellings.

## Softwood

This naturally occurring timber product is grown more in Scandinavian countries, where growth is slower, producing a more structured wood grain. It must be processed then transported to the UK for further manufacture into timber products. Softwood should be purchased locally to save on transport costs. Timber can be used in the following areas of a building: the roof, floor joists and flooring, second fix joinery products, stud walls, windows and doors. Timber can be completely recycled into a further product, such as chipboard.

Using softwood to clad the outside of this building is an attractive and sustainable method that requires no treatment

## Concrete

This is only sustainable in that the finished product has a very long life. Cement production is costly to the environment in terms of energy used and emissions released to the atmosphere. Concrete can be recycled into a crushed hardcore but no recycled materials can be used in its manufacture. Concrete is used in foundations, lintels, floors and some roof structures.

## Common bricks

Common bricks are of lower quality and are used in areas where strength is required but facing bricks aren't needed. They would be used as coursing bricks in internal skins of external walls and as levelling courses under floor joists.

## Facing bricks

These are used where you can see the external brickwork as they look more attractive, but they are more expensive to make. They are mainly used for the external skin of a cavity wall or for garden walls where these have to match the house.

## Engineering bricks

These are hardwearing high-strength bricks that are water-resistant. They are used below DPC level as they are not affected by rising damp. They are an excellent brick to use within drainage manhole construction.

**Activity**

Analyse different types of materials as listed in Table 6.3 used in the construction of domestic and commercial dwellings

**Find out**

Find a local ready-mixed concrete supplier and establish what concrete products they can supply.

**Find out**

Visit a brick manufacturer's website and find out about their sustainable practices.

## Aggregates

These are used for several purposes. Primarily they are constituents of concrete mixes, where a blend of coarse and fine aggregate plus cement and water is mixed to form concrete. A more modern application of aggregates is in external landscaping, where they are used to provide attractive areas that resist water run-off into the main drainage system, thereby adding to sustainable drainage for surface water.

## Glass fibre quilt and mineral wool

These are used to insulate houses and commercial properties. They are used within ceiling voids above and between the joists. External walls use pre-cut 'batts' of mineral wool, which are built at full thickness into the cavity. Internal walls can also use mineral wool, but it must be of a heavier density, so as to resist the passage of sound. This type of insulation is very thermally efficient and will reduce heat loss from a building.

Example of glass-fibre quilt

## Metals

Using stainless steel in many building materials (such as wall ties) helps overcome corrosion problems. Mild-steel products require a secondary process, which could be galvanising, powder-coating or just a layer of paint. Metal is used in other products such as lintels, joist hangers and roof truss fixings, and in aluminum windows. Non-ferrous metals are used in water pipes and fittings.

## Glass

Glass is a versatile material, used mainly in windows. In certain areas, only safety glass can be used. Glass can be manufactured from up to 80% recycled product. It is transported in standard sheet from the factory to the supplier, who then cuts it to size locally. Any waste can be fully recycled, either locally or via the manufacturer.

## Selecting appropriate materials for sustainability

When choosing materials, you should consider a number of factors that impact on energy efficiency and sustainability:

- **Is it recyclable?** Ideally the material selected should be recyclable, at least at the end of its life, as should any wastage generated during its use or installation.

- **Is it local?** If the material is available locally, this reduces the cost of transporting it from the supplier to the construction site.

- **What are the transport implications?** The weight of the product will have an effect on the cost of its transport and the amount of fuels expended in getting it to the site.

- **How much waste is there?** A product that produces no wastage is valuable in terms of not having to throw away valuable resources and the energy that they have used in manufacture.

- **Is it a natural product?** A product that is produced naturally, for example, growing timber can be replenished time and time again.

- **Is it environmentally friendly?** – A material that does not damage the environment in its manufacture and use is a sustainable product that is often referred to as a 'green product'.

- **What is its lifespan?** A longer lifespan, with as little maintenance as possible, means that less energy and resources will have to be put into the product in the future, which saves valuable future resources.

- **Is it worth spending more now?** A material that does not need, for example, painting every five years will save on energy time and costs. Spending a bit more money now will save future expenditure.

## What would you do?

You are working for a client who builds doctors' surgery centres. The current contract you are working on is a large medical centre. You have been asked by the client to recommend the finishes for the front of the centre due to your experience in using current sustainable materials. Assist the client by discussing the advantages of cedar boarding over rendered blockwork.

# Making materials last longer

Many of the materials used in a building project can have their lifespan reduced by the effects of damp, water, frost and chemicals. Treating problems like this early – or, better still, preventing them from happening in the first place – is part and parcel of good environmentally aware building practice.

## The effects of the elements on various building materials

### Masonry

Efflorescence is one cause of the effects of moisture migrating within a new brick structure. Water moves through the mortar into the brick work causing salts to move to the outside of the newly constructed wall, this process is known as primary efflorescence. The water evaporates leaving a white deposit on the surface of the brick. It can be brushed off and the action of weathering will eventually remove the effect.

### Concrete

The effect of water on concrete is to discolour its initial fresh new look from the airborne pollution that is present in the atmosphere and which is picked up within rainfall. Water staining on concrete where the designer has not detailed for the run-off from the building is another obvious effect. Water action within less porous concrete can result in the leaching of alkaline ('lime leaching') through the concrete that form deposits very much like those within cave structures.

An example of efflorescence on brickwork

### Timber – wet and dry rot

This is caused by two different elements. Wet rot is caused by excessive exposure to moisture, which eventually causes the breakdown of the timber cells so that they rot and deteriorate. Dry rot is caused by a fungus that sends out long threads, which attack and eat away at the cells of the timber, causing structural damage.

**Find out**

Have a look at some of the newly constructed houses in your location and see if you can spot some efflorescence appearing on new brickwork.

**Remember**

All of the above defects can be remedied through good design, quality workmanship and materials and effective maintenance.

## Metal

Rust is caused by the oxidation of a ferrous metal. For the reaction to occur, three things must be present: metal, water and oxygen. Rust forms as an orange deposit on the surface of the metal. If it goes untreated, it will continue to eat away at the metal, eventually compromising its strength.

# Particular problems caused by the elements

## Spalling

Spalling is the action of freezing water on the surface of a porous brick. The freezing action causes water to expand, pushing flakes of brickwork from the brick face. The photograph clearly illustrates this action, which leaves the stronger mortar joints proud of the original brickwork face.

The effects of spalling on brickwork

## Thermal expansion

The Building Regulations state clearly the specification for expansion joints within brickwork external walls. These allow the brickwork to expand in the summer months and contract in the winter months without showing signs of cracking. Thermal movement may appear as complete cracks across bricks vertically.

Timber and concrete are good at resisting the affects of frost or freezing water. Exposed timber will maintain its structural integrity for many years. Concrete, once damaged, allows water to enter; if this meets any exposed reinforcing bars, then problems will occur.

## Damp

Damp can cause many problems in a building, and the damage it causes can be costly and difficult to repair. A range of methods and materials can be used to help stop damp getting into a structure.

**DPCs** – placed within the skins of the external walls; always 150 mm above finished ground level.

**Slate** – used traditionally as a barrier to resist the passage of moisture; still found in older external cavity walls; can still be used as a DPC, but commonly replaced by plastic DPC.

**Engineering brick** – Grade A quality brick, so dense it naturally resists the passage of water; can be used below DPC to act as an additional barrier to rising damp.

**Pitch polymer** – a bitumen-type DPC sometimes seen in external walls; can squeeze out of the joint due to pressure and heat; seldom used today.

**PVC** – the most common type of DPC in use today; economical and easy to bed into the joint; often textured to bond to the mortar above and below the joint.

**Did you know?**

Brickwork expansion joints will need taking right through the cavity and the internal block skins.

**Find out**

What do the terms 'Grade A' and 'Grade B' mean on engineering bricks?

**Safety tip**

With any chemical process, always refer to the supplier's safety data sheet for instructions.

**Injected** – chemical DPC is injected into the wall to prevent the passage of moisture; used as a cheap refurbishment technique as you do not have to remove brickwork; internal plaster often removed up to 1 m high and wall replastered with a renovating plaster after injection work is complete.

**DPMs** – placed under floors to prevent rising damp from entering warm floor; tucked into the DPC within the external wall, thus 'tanking' the construction against damp.

**Visqueen** – common trade name for a 1200-gauge plastic product tough enough to withstand tearing but which will bend around corners. Note: hardcore beneath DPM should always be sand-blinded to prevent rupture of DPM.

**Bituthene** – a sheet material manufactured from bitumen that can be laid in sheets, lapped, and used both horizontally and vertically; mainly used for waterproofing basement walls; must be used in accordance with manufacturer's instructions.

## The effects of chemicals on building materials

Concrete can be attacked by certain chemicals.

Carbon dioxide from the air can react with certain chemicals in the concrete. This decreases the protective alkaline which ensures that the steel reinforcement does not rust. Once this bond is broken, then rusting can occur as the concrete expands and spalls away from the reinforcement bars.

Sulphates that come into contact with the cement in concrete can attack the chemical bond of the cement, affecting its strength. **Sulphate-resistant cement (SRC)** and not **ordinary Portland cement (OPC)** must be used where this is a risk: for example, where groundwater is contaminated.

Sulphates can also attack the brickwork cement mortar, especially with a chimney where coal is being burned. Sulphates eat away the cement mortar joints, the reaction causes the joint to expand and the chimney can start to lean over.

Chlorides have been used in the past to alter the setting times of concrete. Unfortunately, over time these affect the strength of concrete, which can have a disastrous effect if the material is under excessive loading conditions.

Alkali silicate is present in some concrete aggregates. This can react with the cement and water and expand, causing a pop-out of the concrete surrounding the reaction. This can have an adverse effect on structural concrete.

Acid rain – a product of burning fossil fuels – also has an effect on certain building materials. Natural stone is mostly affected, as acid rain eats away at the surface of the stone, causing long-term damage.

# Effects of heat and fire on building materials

## *Masonry*

Brickwork and blockwork cope well in a fire within a dwelling or commercial property. Extreme heat can cause masonry to expand and crack but this would be after a substantial time from evacuation of a building. Fire is used in a kiln to harden bricks so they are more than capable of staying stable in a fire. Smoke does, however, cause blackening to the surfaces of bricks and blocks. This can to some degree be washed off but may leave a permanent stain that requires decoration internally and power washing externally.

Water, as we have seen previously, when combined with a frost or freezing conditions causes spalling to the surface of the brickwork or the breakdown of the mortar joint due to weathering.

## *Concrete*

Concrete can spall under the influence of fire. If the reinforcement lies near to the surface of the concrete and this heats up then it will expand at a different rate to the surrounding concrete. This expansion can cause cracking to the concrete structure. Concrete is fairly resilient to water damage and will dry out after wetting; but if the water contains contaminants then this can lead to the chemical attack of the cement within the concrete.

## *Timber*

Heat and the presence of oxygen cause the combustion of timber by fire. The surface chars and eventually breaks down the structural integrity of the timber until it is burnt right through. Smoke damage can discolour timber which will then require decoration if it has not caught fire and charred. Water can damage timber by wetting which expands the hygroscopic material and causes dimensional change to the timber, which will eventually rot if this wetting persists.

## *Metal*

Metal does not react well in a fire. As it heats up the molecular structure weakens and it loses up to half its strength at over 500 degrees. This can cause the collapse of structures as the steel melts slightly and warps under extreme heat. However, this does take some time and may not affect the evacuation of a structure. Water reacts with exposed metal, as we have seen, to form rust. Surface rust is not harmful but continual exposure to the elements of unprotected metal will result in severe corrosion.

**Find out**

Consult your local newspaper's website and look up a building fire that has occurred in your area. Look for photographs to see what damage was caused.

**Remember**

Building Regulations will make provisions for the building structure in the event of a fire.

# Treating building materials to prevent the effects of deterioration

### Intumescent paint

This is a chemical-based paint that reacts with high temperatures. It foams and expands around the steelwork it is painted upon to protect it from the heat giving the occupants time to escape.

Treated timber decking

### Paints

These are used to protect timber, brickwork, and metal work from the effects of water. They form a microscopic seal across the surface preventing water penetration past this layer.

### Water repellant

This can be painted onto the surface of exposed brickwork to allow water to run off the brick face more easily. This prevents it standing and absorbing into the brickwork. Where if it freezes, it can become a problem as we have seen.

### Vac Vac and tanalising

These are chemical pressure impregnation systems to chemically treat timber from fungi and insect attack. They fill the pore holes within the timber and kill off any wood-boring insect that attacks its structure. Fungi includes the dry rot spores and other cellulous eating organisms.

This timber treatment alters the colour of the natural timber often to a green shade.

### Sulphate-resistant cement (SRC)

This is a cement that contains chemicals and mineral aggregates which resists the attack of sulphates within concrete and is used where this is detected by testing.

### Injected damp proof courses

These use chemicals of various kinds and mixtures to form a chemical barrier within the brickwork after they have cured and filled the pores in the bricks. These have to be injected through holes drilled into the outer wall and sometimes in inner walls.

# Rectifying and preventing deterioration

## Masonry and concrete

Masonry and concrete make a movement joint that allows the brick and block panels to expand and contract under thermal movement. A compressible board is used within the joint which is sealed with a polysulphide joint to prevent water ingress. Joints within concrete slabs are very similar but the Flexcell is replaced with a material that is more resilient.

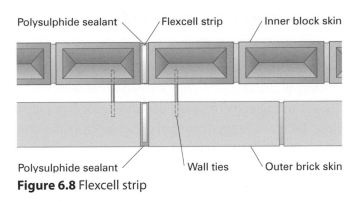

Polysulphide sealant · Flexcell strip · Inner block skin

Polysulphide sealant · Wall ties · Outer brick skin

**Figure 6.8** Flexcell strip

## Timber

Cutting and splicing in new timber is an age-old prevention method that saves having to remove the whole length of timber, manufacture a new piece and refit. Timber can be initially protected by pressure impregnation or it can be simply painted or stained using a flexible coating as the timber will expand and contract. This method of coating must be maintained to extend the lifespan of the timber and any damaged areas repaired quickly.

Insecticides or fungicidal washes will remove mould growth on timber but ventilation and quick drying of wet surfaces is the key to preventing this damage.

## Methods used on metals to give galvanic protection and protective coatings

Galvanising using a hot dip process provides a good layer of protection to ordinary mild steel. The steel is fed through a bath of molten zinc, which coats the metal and gives it long lasting protection against water damage.

High-quality paints that are developed for bonding to steel work should be used instead of galvanising where colour is required. A primer base coat is applied followed by several other coats that build up the film of paint. Powder coating steelwork is another process that can be used to coat the steel with a colour protective layer.

**Find out**

Have a look around at the built environment where you live and work. Analyse the brick and concrete buildings and see where the movement joints have been formed.

**Find out**

Find out the largest size of steelwork that can be powder-coated, and gather some pictures of examples.

## Effects of adverse weather on building materials used in domestic and commercial dwellings

### *Driving rain, snow and wind*

Water can be driven into a structure and this can occur in several ways: through the roof tiles and onto the underlay, through open windows or poor seals or through badly maintained brickwork mortar joints. This can lead to damage. The recent spate of floods within the UK have shown just what damage can occur to a property even if the water did not enter the ground floor. Excessive rising damp can occur which causes damage to internal finishes, timber wall plates and floor timbers if the water contains sewage particles. High volumes of floodwaters can cause buildings to move on their foundations from the water pressure or can, in fact, push over walls.

High levels of snowfall can produce heavy loads on structures that could lead to cracking or collapse of the roof structure. High winds each autumn also account for some damage to chimneys and walls as brickwork is blown over.

# Knowledge refresher

1   Identify a sustainable material with reasons for your choice.

2   How would you identify if a material is sustainable?

3   What effect does water have on timber?

4   Does anything have to be done with brickwork panels for movement?

5   Why would timber be chemically treated?

6   What method could be used to protect mild steel?

7   What does fire do to steel beams?

# chapter 7

# Complex masonry structures

## OVERVIEW

The term 'complex masonry structures' refers to any brickwork or stone work that requires intricate, and sometimes difficult, setting out procedures. It also refers to brickwork or stone work where decorative features have been incorporated within a structure to provide support and enhance aesthetic value (aesthetic means 'the principles of beauty, taste and art').

Most decorative features play no part in providing support to a structure, and are constructed purely to improve the aesthetic value. These types of feature are dealt with in Chapter 9.

In this chapter, we will look mainly at the setting out details required for more intricate work, such as curved brickwork and angled brickwork. We will also look at the methods of providing structural support that also enhances the appearance of brickwork structures.

This chapter will cover:

- corbelling
- curved brickwork
- angled and splayed brickwork (including raking cuts)
- special-shaped or purpose-made bricks
- reinforced brickwork.

Corbelling and soldier courses

# Corbelling

Traditionally, corbelling was used as a method of providing structural support for brickwork extending in front of the main walling. However, corbelling details are also used to enhance the appearance of brickwork structures, and have been for many years.

In fact, corbelling has been used since Neolithic times. In medieval times, it was widely used to provide support for upper storeys, parapets or turrets projecting from strongholds. Early forms of corbelling were made from stones that were keyed deep into the main walling, often carved with elaborate designs, depicting human faces, animals, demons or floral themes.

Corbelling used as the shoulder of a gable end

Corbelling at a certain position in a length of walling

In more modern times, corbelling has had a wide range of uses: for example, reducing the opening size at the top of manholes and sewer chambers, to accommodate standard-sized covers and frames. However, these days this is achieved using precast concrete reducing slabs. A bricklayer may still be required to form corbelling at the heads of manholes where existing corbelling has been partially dislodged, or has perished over the years and requires repair or reinstatement.

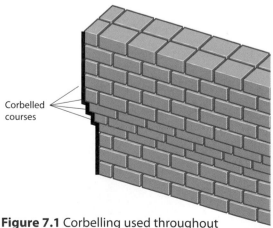

Corbelled courses

**Figure 7.1** Corbelling used throughout the length of the brickwork structure

Corbelling can be used at certain positions in a length of walling or can be continuous throughout the length of the walling.

All types of corbelling work must be carefully planned and carried out to satisfy both the structural design requirements of the project and the British Standards Institution Codes of Practice.

## Methods for constructing traditional corbels

The overhang measurement for each course of a brick corbel should be equal. In all instances, the measurement shown on the detailed drawing provided by the architect should be adhered to. However, the two most common measurements used for the overhang of individual courses is either 28 mm or 56 mm.

It is essential when constructing a corbel that plumb and level are accurately maintained. It is also important to maintain equal projections for each course and as a rule of thumb, the total projection of the entire corbel should not exceed the thickness of the main wall.

When tying the corbel bricks into the main wall, you should endeavour to achieve the maximum lap with the course below and wherever possible headers should be used for the corbelled bricks, particularly for a corbel where larger projections are used (quarter brick overhang).

Course 1

Course 2

When building any corbel it is important to lay the bricks from the back of the main wall through to the front of the corbel. This allows the back of the corbelled bricks below to be held or weighted down as quickly as possible to prevent them **tipping** forward.

The accompanying photographs show the preferred bonding arrangements for a corbel with a quarter brick overhang per course.

Course 3

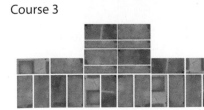

Course 4

Completed corbelling

As each course is constructed the bricklayer must ensure that the corbel is square to the main wall. This can be achieved with the aid of a building square.

It is also important that each course is levelled on the underside of the corbelled bricks as this is the line that will be seen.

Where a continuous corbel is being built, a line is used on the underside edge of the corbel to maintain a face plane.

## Corbelling in timber- and steel-framed buildings

Traditional methods of constructing corbels cannot be applied successfully in many modern

Using a building square

construction systems, such as timber- and steel-framed buildings, where brickwork cladding is used to form cavity walling. These need specially designed brickwork support systems, along with purpose-made bricks, in most instances, to form the corbelled feature and mask the support system adequately.

Additional care must be taken when forming corbelled features using this method. Temporary support for the purpose-made bricks will need to be provided during construction to prevent 'tipping' of the bricks. Each corbel course is required to be tied back to the structure at every bed joint. Any brickwork laid above the corbelled course will be carried by a suitable type of support system. Examples of these support systems can be found in Chapter 20: Erecting Masonry Cladding of *Brickwork NVQ and Technical Certificate Level 2*.

## FAQ

*Why construct corbels in brick? Would it not be easier to use pre-formed corbels made from concrete or stone or even cast concrete corbels in situ using formwork?*

It would be much easier to use pre-formed or cast in situ corbels. However, these do not always blend aesthetically within a structure where brick is required to be of a very high quality and may appear as an unsightly break in these types of structures.

## Knowledge refresher

1. What is meant by the term 'complex masonry structures'?

2. In recent years, what has replaced brick corbelling as a way of reducing the opening size at the top of manholes?

3. What could be the result of failing to plan effectively and follow the requirements for bonding when building corbelling?

4. Why might you tilt the front corbel bricks backwards slightly as you lay them?

## What would you do?

You are in the final stages of constructing a brick corbel and have cut one of the bricks, which ties into the main wall, too short. You have just put away all your cutting tools, as this was the last cut. Should you use the brick you have cut and fill the void with strong mortar, or should you cut a new brick to the correct size? What are the consequences of each of the actions you may choose?

# Curved brickwork

Brickwork can be curved either on plan or in **elevation**. Arches are a typical example of brickwork curved in elevation. This section will deal with other forms of curved work in elevation and also brickwork curved on plan.

## Brickwork curved in elevation

There are two methods of constructing curved brickwork in elevation and they are:

1   **convex**

2   **concave**.

### Constructing convex curved brickwork

This type of curved work is produced with the aid of a short length of timber pointed at one end and fixed to the face of the wall – this length of timber is referred to as a trammel.

The point at which the trammel is fixed to the face of the wall is known as the pivot point.

The trammel can be fixed to a timber plate, which is secured to the brickwork with the use of nails driven into the bed joints. When fixing the trammel to the timber plate you must ensure that it is not fixed tightly against the plate, preventing it from turning easily.

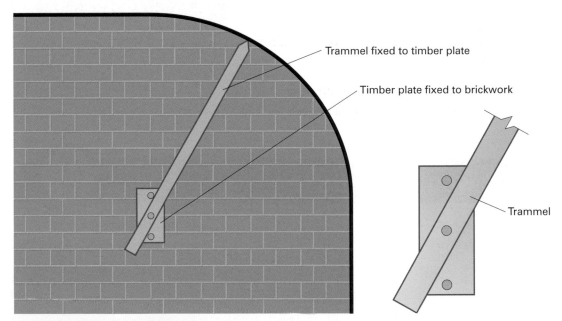

Trammel fixed to timber plate

Timber plate fixed to brickwork

Trammel

**Figure 7.2** A trammel in place

The bricks to be cut in order to form the curve are placed in position, dry and on top of a piece of timber or other suitable material at a thickness of 10 mm to simulate the bed joint thickness. The vertical joint thickness must also be allowed for.

The trammel is then swung round across the face of the positioned brick and marked with a pencil or suitable marker. Once the brick has been cut it can be laid and checked for accuracy by again swinging the trammel across the face.

A brick laid on edge is the most common way to provide the finish or capping to this type of curved brickwork, unless of course it is used as a decorative feature within a length of walling which is to be continued in height

Depending on the severity of the curve, the brick-on-edge can either be laid with V-shaped joints or the bricks are cut to a V shape to prevent oversized joints.

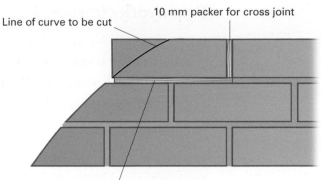

**Figure 7.3** The use of a 10 mm packing to allow for joint thickness

## Constructing concave curved brickwork

Again, a trammel will need to be used to establish the cuts required to form the curve. However, the trammel needs to be positioned and secured in a completely different way.

Before the trammel can be positioned, the main walling will need to be built to the height of the striking point. Once this height has been reached the trammel can be positioned.

The trammel is fixed onto a timber support held in position on the top course by either a brick or block weight.

The same principles used in forming the convex curve are then applied to this type of construction. This also includes the forming of the brick-on-edge course.

Concave curved brickwork

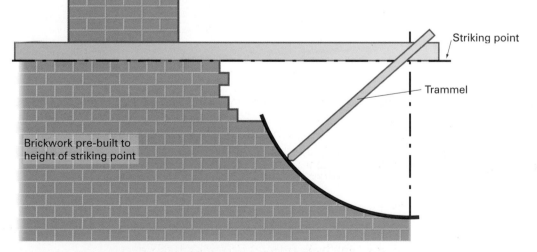

**Figure 7.4** The positioning of a trammel, and its timber support, for the construction of a concave curve

## Brickwork curved on plan

Brickwork which is curved on plan can be used in a number of situations. These include constructing brickwork to support bay windows, boundary walls which have to follow the curvature of roads and pathways and for numerous decorative features such as flower beds, etc.

There are a number of methods used in constructing this type of walling. The choice of which method to use depends on the size of the curved wall to be built and the work space available.

However, whichever method is used, the rules for both plumbing and levelling the brickwork remain the same. With walls curved on plan it is essential that plumbing and levelling are accurate throughout the construction of the walling. If accuracy is not maintained, the end product will be unsightly and it is highly unlikely that the desired curvature of the wall will be achieved.

On any curved wall, plumbing points will need to be established at various intervals around the length of the curve. Although the length of the curve will determine the amount of plumbing points required these should be no more than 1 m to 1.2 m apart.

Levelling across the top of the wall should always be carried between the plumbing points.

Where the curves to be constructed are relatively small, a small timber template can be used. This template is cut accurately to fit around the curved face of the wall and will need to be cut to a length which allows it to fit between the plumbing points.

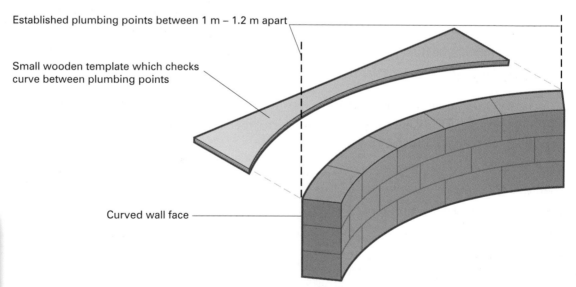

Established plumbing points between 1 m – 1.2 m apart

Small wooden template which checks curve between plumbing points

Curved wall face

**Figure 7.5** Established plumbing points and method of levelling for curved walls

Larger templates can be produced for constructing bay windows. These templates would be designed to sit on the top of each course to be built and give both the curve for the outside face of the curved bay and the line of the main wall.

**Note**

No matter what type of template is used, it is essential that you ensure that all bricks sit against the template when you are carrying out checks using it.

The other method used to help in the construction of curved walls is the trammel. We have already seen the way in which a trammel is used to aid cutting and check the accuracy of curved walling earlier in this chapter and the principle is the same. However, a trammel can only be used where there is sufficient space to establish the pivoting point. The position of the pivot point can be determined from the detailed drawings provided on site. The trammel can be used for either the internal or external face of the curve.

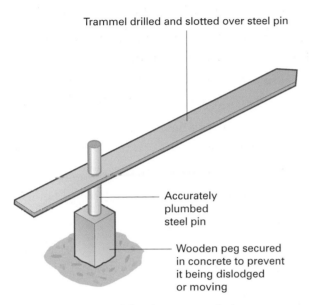

Trammel drilled and slotted over steel pin

Accurately plumbed steel pin

Wooden peg secured in concrete to prevent it being dislodged or moving

**Figure 7.6** A trammel fixed over a steel pin

The trammel is fixed by one end being drilled to allow it to be dropped over a steel pin representing the pivot point. This steel pin should be seated in the top of a wooden peg, which in turn is set in concrete to prevent it from moving whilst in use.

Although stretchers are used in curved walling, the most common bond used is header bond. Stretcher bond can be used in curved walls. However, the stretchers may have to be cut on the back face, where the curve is too tight to allow the use of full stretchers, so as not to affect the trueness of the curve.

> **Note**
>
> When using either stretcher or header bond, V-shaped cross joints have to be used in order to ensure the bricks follow the desired curve line.

## Header bond

Depending on the severity of the curve, full headers can be used throughout the length of each course. However, where the curve is smaller or tighter, snap headers have to be used in order to maintain a true curve. Where this is the case, a full header is used every third brick. This practice prevents oversized V-shaped joints which make the wall look unsightly.

Where both sides of a curved wall need to have a good face, it is advisable to use purpose-made Radial bricks. These are available in both headers and stretchers.

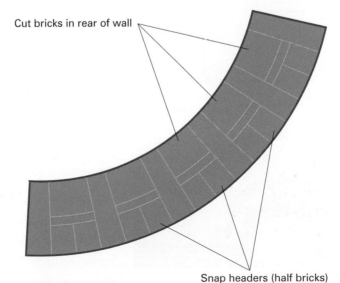

Cut bricks in rear of wall

Snap headers (half bricks)

**Figure 7.7** Using snap headers when constructing curved walling in header bond

**Note**

The use of these bricks also removes the need for V-shaped joints.

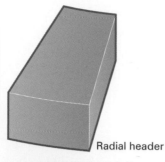

Radial header

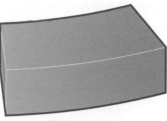

Radial stretcher

**Figure 7.8** Radial header and stretcher bricks

## Serpentine walls

As the name suggests, this type of walling turns in and out along its length giving a snaking effect. The curves are set out and constructed using the methods described earlier in this chapter.

Serpentine walling snaking in and out throughout its length

**Figure 7.9** A plan view of a serpentine wall

## Axed arches

Axed arches are constructed from cut bricks as opposed to the wedge or V-shaped joints used in the construction of rough ringed arches.

An axed arch

The use of arch construction in modern day building projects is far less common than it was and more often than not, where arch construction is incorporated into a building, purpose-made bricks are used. Purpose-made bricks remove the need for bricks to be cut on site which can be time consuming and generate a high percentage of wasted bricks through the cutting process. Another major advantage with using purpose-made voussoirs or arch-bricks is that they are uniform in shape and their dimensions are accurate.

However, where there is a requirement for voussoirs to be cut by hand, a template must be made to establish the shape of them. The template itself will need to be traversed across the face of the arch in order to provide the exact shape required for each of the voussoirs.

## Cutting an axed arch

The traditional method of producing axed brick arches is to cut bricks to shape using a hammer and bolster, measuring them against a templet of the voussoir shape required.

## How to make the templet

The tools required to make an accurate templet:

- trammel heads
- dividers
- bevel
- traversing rules
- measuring rule
- straight edge
- carpenter's tools for cutting wood templet.

The templet is usually made from timber of between 6 mm and 12 mm thickness.

The first step is to draw the arch full size on a sheet of plywood.

**Figure 7.10** Setting out an axed arch

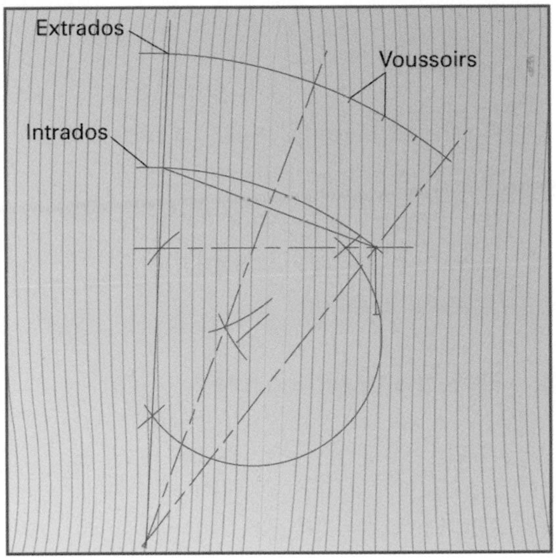

Set out a centre line and then another line at right angles to this (known as the 'springing line'). Find out the springing point and draw intrados, extrados and skewback lines.

Set the dividers to the size of the brick being used in the arch, and mark out voussoirs on the extrados.

Based on the full size drawing of the arch, mark out the templet onto plywood, to project approximately 50 mm above the extrados and 150 mm below the intrados, which will allow for any adjustment that may need to be made during traversing the arch.

**Figure 7.11** Templet

**Note**

You only need to set out half of the arch, to include the key brick.

**Note**

Once the dividers have been set, do not open them any further as any templet based on this voussoir shape will be incorrect and any bricks cut to this templet will be too narrow to fit the actual arch.

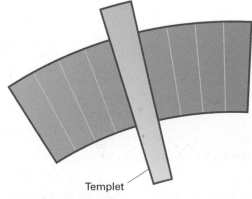

## Traversing the arch

At this stage the templet only provides a rough guide. To obtain an accurate shape, the templet must be traversed over the face of the arch, to highlight any small errors in the shape.

To traverse the arch, follow the steps below.

1. Place the **traversing** rule A to the key brick.

2. Arrange the templet to fit a voussoir and mark a line on the side of the templet to coincide with the intrados. This is called the 'traversing mark'.

3. Place the traversing rule B.

4. Remove A and the templet.

5. Place A to B.

6. Remove B and again fit templet, allowing traversing mark to coincide with the intrados.

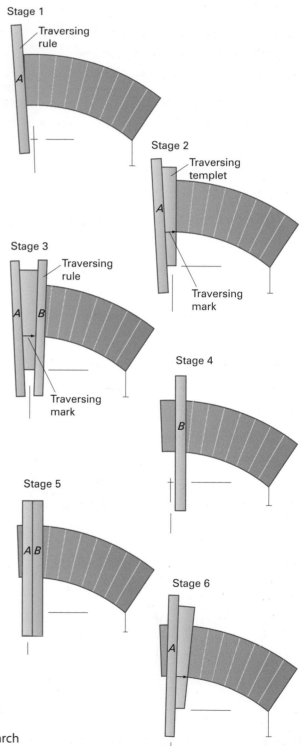

**Figure 7.12** Traversing a templet for an axed arch

If the templet reaches the top of the skewback (the extrados) before it reaches the bottom (the intrados), it must be made smaller at the top. If it reaches the bottom before the top, then it must be planed down at the bottom. If there is space left over between the templet edge and the skewback, then the template must be lowered so that the traversing mark is higher up the templet. If it overruns the skewback, then the templet needs to be raised so that the traversing mark is lower down.

Traversing the arch must be repeated until the templet fits exactly between the key and the skewback. This means that the templet will be accurate and the voussoirs cut using it will be the exact shape required to complete the axed arch.

Once the exact shape of the voussoirs has been established, construction of the arch can begin. We have already dealt with the process of setting up the temporary arch support or arch centre in *Brickwork Level 2*.

Having set up the arch centre, the position of the key brick needs to be marked on the face of the arch centre.

The next step is to mark the remaining brick spaces plus one joint either side of the key brick. This can be done accurately with dividers.

The first brick is bedded against the skewback and lined in from the striking point through the voussoir gauge mark, identified on the arch centre. You then continue to bed the remaining voussoirs alternately on either side of the key brick. This will prevent any unnecessary overloading on either side of the arch centre.

It is important to remember to follow the markings for each brick as the work proceeds.

The arch bricks should be frequently checked for square with a straight edge or, alternatively, a line should be used across the face of the arch.

**Remember**

Keep the top of the arch centre free from mortar to prevent unsightly mortar staining on the underneath of the arch bricks once it has been removed.

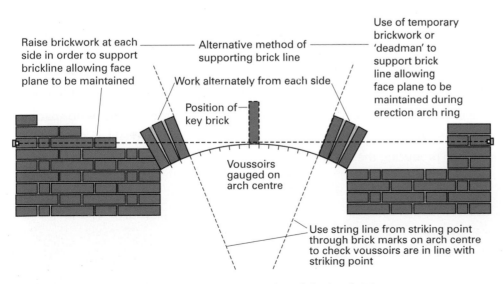

Raise brickwork at each side in order to support brickline allowing face plane to be maintained

Alternative method of supporting brick line

Use of temporary brickwork or 'deadman' to support brick line allowing face plane to be maintained during erection arch ring

Work alternately from each side

Position of key brick

Voussoirs gauged on arch centre

Use string line from striking point through brick marks on arch centre to check voussoirs are in line with striking point

**Figure 7.13** Bricks being laid from alternate sides of the key brick

## FAQ

*Could a piece of string or bricklaying line, fixed at the pivot point, be used instead of a wooden trammel when checking or marking the face of a curved wall either on plan or in elevation?*

This is not good practice as there is a possibility that the line may stretch during use giving a false reading, or if the line is not kept taut, again a false reading will be given.

## Definition

**Acute angle** – this is an angle less than 90°

**Obtuse angle** – this is an angle greater than 90°

# Angled and splayed brickwork

Not all buildings, boundary walls and garden walls are built with 90° or right angled returns. In some instances it is necessary to build walls at angles to each other in order to follow the lines or boundaries of the site.

Angles at which walls are built other than 90° are known as either acute or obtuse angles.

Where **acute** or **obtuse angles** are to be used on site, the angles have normally been established by the architect. In most instances, special-shaped, purpose-made bricks will be supplied for the construction of angled walls. However, it is not uncommon to see acute angles constructed from bricks cut on site. It is highly unlikely that a bricklayer would be expected to cut these angled bricks with normal hand tools as this would undoubtedly result in a large number of wasted bricks. Where these bricks are required to be cut on site, a table saw would be used. It is also important to note that where bricks are cut on site, these bricks should be solid, as bricks with a frog or holes would be virtually impossible to cut to the desired angles.

## Acute angles

A number of bonding arrangements for acute angles are shown below.

In walls of 1 brick thickness, acute angles can be produced by bringing the corner of the angled brick structure to a sharp point or, alternatively, they can be produced by using special-shaped bricks which remove the sharp point. Again, the method to be used will be determined by the architect when producing the drawings.

## Method 1 – corners produced with a sharp point

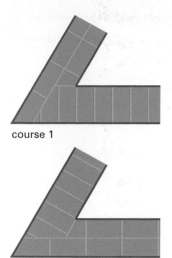

course 1

course 2

**Figure 7.14** Bonding arrangement for 1 brick thick wall in English bond

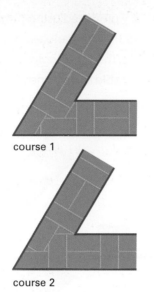

course 1

course 2

**Figure 7.15** Bonding arrangement for 1 brick thick wall in Flemish bond

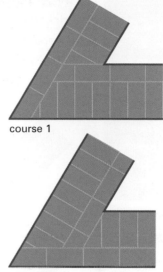

course 1

course 2

**Figure 7.16** Bonding arrangement for 1½ brick thick wall in English bond

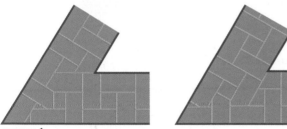

course 1          course 2

**Figure 7.17** Bonding arrangement for 1½ brick thick wall in Flemish bond

## Method 2 – special-shaped bricks used to avoid sharp point at the corner

Where walls of more than 1 brick in thickness are constructed, a further alternative finish can be provided to the corner. In this method both the sharp point and the use of purpose-made bricks are avoided. This is referred to as 'bird's mouth' corner.

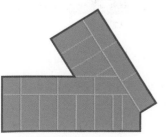

Plan of course 1

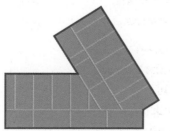

Plan of course 2

**Figure 7.18** Bonding arrangement for 1½ brick thick wall in English bond

# External obtuse angles

These types of angles are normally produced using purpose-made bricks known as 'squint' bricks (See Figure 7.33 on page 193). Where angles are required which are not the normal ones covered by the use of squint bricks, then the angles will have to be produced by cutting the bricks on site (again a mechanical table saw will need to be used).

Shown below are a number of bonding arrangements used for producing obtuse angles.

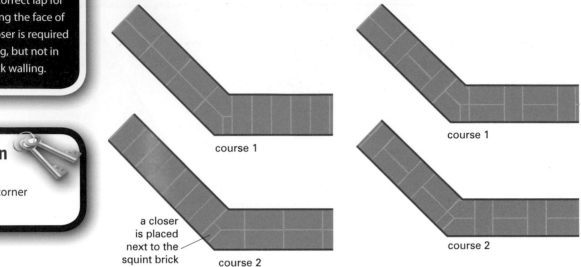

course 1

a closer is placed next to the squint brick

course 2

course 1

course 2

**Figure 7.19** Bonding arrangement for 1 brick thick wall in English bond

**Figure 7.20** Bonding arrangement for 1 brick thick wall in Flemish bond

As with acute angles, an alternative method can be used at the **quoin** in order to avoid using costly, special shaped bricks.

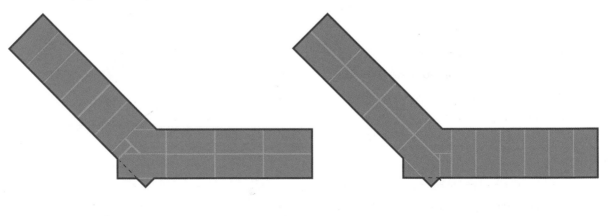

Plan of course 1

Plan of course 2

**Figure 7.21** Bonding arrangement for the alternative to using squint bricks in a 1 brick thick wall in English bond

# Internal obtuse angles

The preferred method of constructing internal obtuse angles is by using a purpose-made brick known as a 'dogleg' (See Figure 7.34 on page 193). The dogleg brick provides a much stronger joint at the intersection of the two lengths of walling.

Using standard, cut bricks can produce a weakness at the intersection of the two walls if the cuts are not accurate and are not lapped correctly.

Shown below are a number of bonding arrangements used for producing internal obtuse angles.

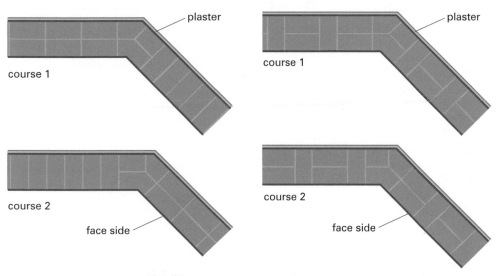

**Figure 7.22** Bonding arrangement for 1 brick thick wall in English bond

**Figure 7.23** Bonding arrangement for 1 brick thick wall in Flemish bond

# Tumbling-in

Although not commonly seen in modern building projects, tumbling-in was an effective and decorative method of reducing the width of supporting piers or buttresses on retaining or large boundary walls. It was also used in reducing the width of external chimney breasts.

One simple method of reducing the thickness of a wall or pier is to use plinth bricks. However, the face of the angled brickwork is not as appealing to the eye as it is with tumbling-in using standard cut bricks. This is because the face of the work completed with plinth bricks will have small ridges formed by the shape of the plinths.

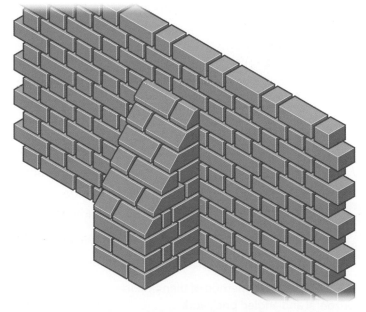

**Figure 7.24** Plinth bricks being used to reduce the thickness of a pier

## Method of tumbling-in using standard cut bricks

Where tumbling-in is only required for a short reduction, the angle and cuts can be set out on a large piece of plywood. The angle can then be maintained with the use of a small template cut in the shape of a gun, to the angle required.

For larger reductions where the work cannot be set out on a board, it is necessary to position lines at either side of the tumbling-in. These lines are fixed in place with the use of battens. The positioning of these battens, along with the lines, is shown in Figure 7.26.

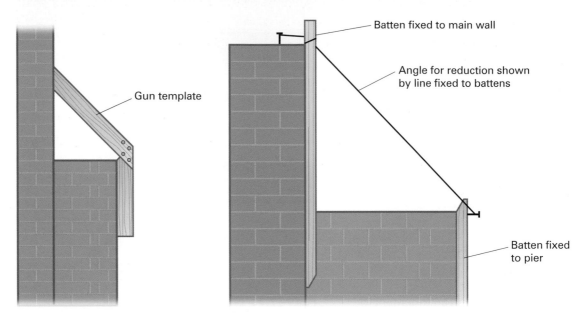

Gun template

Batten fixed to main wall

Angle for reduction shown by line fixed to battens

Batten fixed to pier

**Figure 7.25** 'Gun' template used to maintain slope of reduction

**Figure 7.26** The position of battens for fixing lines

Once the lines are fixed, a gun template can be made to the angle required and this, as with the previous method described, is used to check and maintain the correct angle throughout the run of tumbling-in.

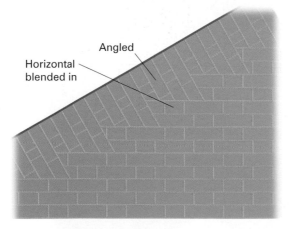

Angled

Horizontal blended in

**Figure 7.27** A preferred method of blending in the horizontal and angled brickwork

When starting it is essential that the first course is laid so that it overhangs the brickwork below in order to provide a weathering. This overhang must be provided for when positioning the batten, by extending it past the actual striking point.

It is most important that, as the work proceeds, a gauge rod is used throughout the length of the tumbling-in: failure to maintain gauge would result in unsightly split courses at the top of the tumbling-in.

Where there is a large length of tumbling-in, it is best practice to extend the horizontal brickwork of the pier or buttress to give the impression of both the tumbling-in and the pier brickwork blending into each other. This is shown in Figure 7.27.

# Raking cutting

## Gable ends

The most common situation where raking cutting is used is when constructing a gable end.

When constructing a gable end, temporary profiles are required in order to establish the angle of the raking cut and provide a guide for the bricks to be cut. These profiles are in the form of temporary roof trusses or rafters and are positioned immediately behind the wall to be built. The height and pitch of the truss or rafters will have already been determined and this information will be included on the relevant drawings.

A typical brick gable end

A bracket or short length of ridge board is fixed at the top of the profile in order to extend the point of the apex out far enough so that lines can be attached to establish the cutting line.

Once the lines have been set up and the angle of the raking cut has been established, the main walling is constructed and raked back to leave just the spaces for the bricks to be cut.

Temporarily bed the brick to be cut. Mark the brick with a pencil at the points, top and bottom, where the line crosses the face of the brick.

Once marked, draw the cutting line across the face of the brick by joining the two previously marked points together. The marking must be transferred to the back face of the brick to ensure that an accurate cut is obtained across the width of the brick.

Trim any excess from the top of the brick using a scutch hammer. Now the brick is ready to be laid to the line.

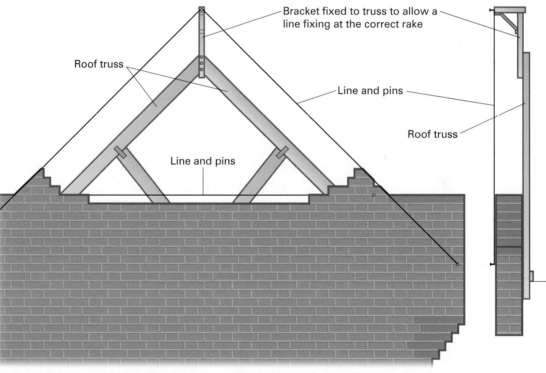

**Figure 7.28** The position of temporary profiles (truss/rafters) and lines

## Knowledge refresher

1. What is an acute angle?

2. What is the name given to the special-shaped template used when tumbling in?

3. What is the most common situation where raking cuts are used?

4. Describe a 'serpentine wall'?

## What would you do?

You are half way through the construction of a curved section of walling and you are using a timber trammel to aid with the marking of the bricks to be cut. Due to a knot in the timber the trammel breaks and can no longer be used. The alternatives are to either spend time producing a new timber trammel or use a bricklaying line of the same length as the trammel and attach this to exactly the same point as the trammel was attached.

Which of the alternatives would you choose and why?

# Special-shaped or purpose-made bricks

We have already dealt briefly with a number of special or purpose-made bricks earlier in this chapter – squints, doglegs and plinths. However, there are many variations to these bricks and the number that is actually available is endless and all have their own specific use.

The following is a brief introduction to just some of the brick specials available.

## Plinth bricks

These are used to reduce the thickness of walls vertically.

### Find Out

Search the websites of leading brick manufacturers to find full details of the varieties of special made bricks currently available.

**Figure 7.29** A plinth stretcher

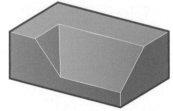

**Figure 7.30** A plinth header

**Figure 7.31** External plinth return

**Figure 7.32** Internal plinth return

## Squint bricks

These are used for acute and obtuse angles.

**Figure 7.33** Squint brick

**Figure 7.34** Dogleg brick (used for internal angles)

## Cant bricks

These are used where corners need to be chamfered.

**Figure 7.35** Cant brick

**Figure 7.36** Double cant brick

### Definition

**Cant** – meaning bevelled, sloped or tilted

## Bull-nose bricks

These are used where the corners need to be rounded.

**Figure 7.37** Single bull-nose

**Figure 7.38** Double bull-nose

## Capping and coping bricks

These are used to provide a weathering and pleasing finish to the tops of walls.

**Figure 7.39** Special made brick coping (saddleback)

**Figure 7.40** Special made brick coping (rounded)

## Bonding bricks

These are pre-made standard brick cuts. They are normally made to prevent unnecessary cutting and save on wastage of bricks. These cuts are extremely accurate and are normally used where appearance of the finished article is required to be almost perfect.

**Figure 7.41** Half batt

**Figure 7.42** Three quarter batt

**Figure 7.43** Queen closer

**Figure 7.44** King closer

## Arch and radial bricks

As the name suggests these are used when constructing feature arches and curved brickwork.

**Figure 7.45** Radial brick

**Figure 7.46** Voussoir or arch brick

## Slip bricks

These are used where a split course of bricks needs to be introduced into a length of walling.

## Cill bricks

Again, as the name suggests these are used to form window and door cills.

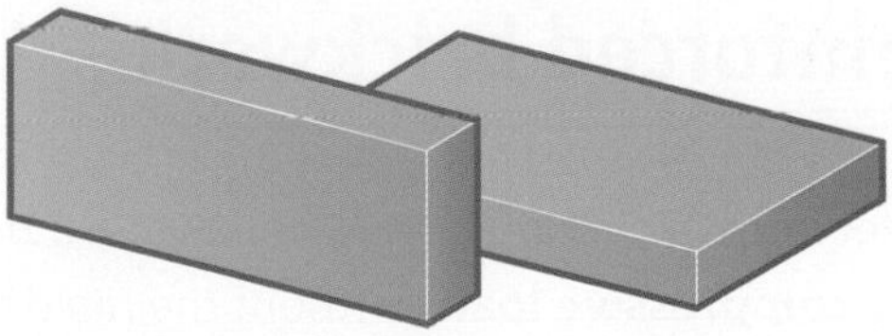

**Figure 7.47** Slip bricks

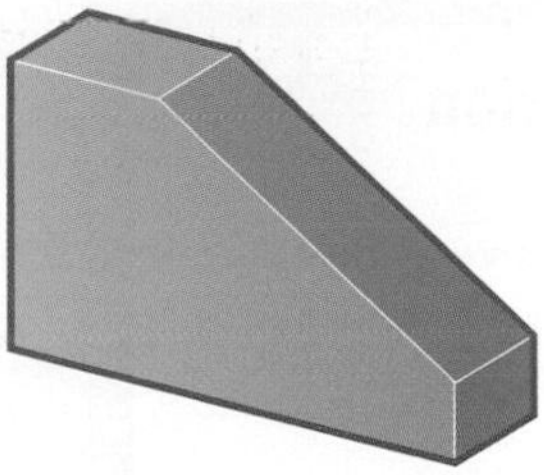

**Figure 7.48** Standard cill brick

# Knowledge refresher

1. What type of special-shaped brick would be used for constructing an external obtuse angle?

2. For what purpose would you use a 'dogleg' brick?

3. For what purpose would you use a 'bull-nose' brick?

4. State the main purpose of coping and capping bricks.

# What would you do?

Joe, a recently qualified bricklayer, is working with a gang constructing a boundary wall, one end finished with a curved ramp feature. Joe has been asked to mark and cut the bricks for the curve. He has been told that the bricks can only be cut using the mechanical table saw on site. Although he has been trained and deemed competent in the use of the table saw, he has never been trained in the process of changing a saw blade.

Halfway through the cutting job, the saw blade starts chipping the face of the bricks, and is taking longer than normal to cut through the bricks.

What is the possible cause of the bricks becoming damaged and the process taking longer? How should the problem be rectified? Should Joe carry out any necessary remedial work on the saw?

# Reinforced brickwork

Under normal circumstances, brickwork, if bonded correctly, is more than strong enough to carry **compressive loads** without the need for additional reinforcement. However, brickwork structures can also be subjected to **tensile stress**, where lateral loads or forces are imposed on the brickwork structure, such as high winds, or heavy loads that must be supported by the face of a structure.

Where brickwork structures are exposed to tensile stress, something must be done to strengthen the brickwork and prevent it failing, which could result in cracking and even the collapse of the structure. Steel reinforcement is one of the most common ways of providing the necessary additional strength. However, structural engineers are needed to determine the right method for each situation.

One of the most commonly used types of steel reinforcement is bed joint reinforcement. This is laid in the mortar bed to counteract movement in the brickwork. When laying steel reinforcement in the bed joints, it is important that a minimum of 15 mm space is left between the face of the brickwork and the edge of the reinforcement mesh. This is to ensure that the steel is fully surrounded by mortar to protect it from exposure and subsequent corrosion.

However, steel reinforcement has its limitations, and is not suitable for structures subject to persistent and severe tensile stresses, such as retaining excessive volumes of soil, or where boundary walls may be subjected to impact. In these types of situations, you will need to use other methods of providing lateral support to the structure.

One bonding arrangement that incorporates steel reinforcing rods is Quetta bond reinforced brickwork.

## Quetta bond reinforced brickwork

This method uses vertical steel reinforcement rods contained in 'pockets', formed in the middle of solid walls using either Flemish or Flemish garden wall bond.

The vertical steel reinforcement rods should be attached to starter bars, incorporated at the base of the wall to tie the vertical bars within the wall to the foundation. As construction of the brickwork progresses, the pockets containing the rods are filled with a particular mortar or concrete mix, which will stabilise the rods and form a bond between the rods and the brickwork. The mortar should be compacted well

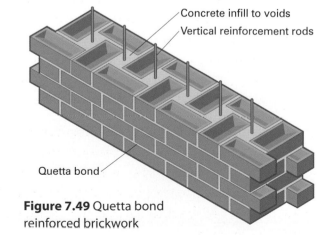

Concrete infill to voids
Vertical reinforcement rods
Quetta bond

**Figure 7.49** Quetta bond reinforced brickwork

around the rods so that the pocket is fully filled and there is sufficient bond between the rods and the brickwork.

This method also has its limitations, and can only be used where the walls are of a 1½-brick thickness.

## Pockets on the retaining side of the wall

An alternative to Quetta bond is to provide pockets containing reinforcement rods encased in concrete on the retaining side of the wall. These pockets will not be visible, as they will be covered by the soil being retained. This method allows a solid wall to be reduced in thickness towards the top of the wall, saving on the amount of materials that need to be used without affecting the stability of the structure.

As with Quetta bond, the vertical steel reinforcement rods are fixed to starter bars incorporated in the foundation concrete. However, with this method, the vertical reinforcement rods can be left until the construction of the brickwork is complete. Shuttering is then placed against the pocket and filled with a suitable concrete mix. This concrete must again be compacted well to make sure the steel rods are properly protected.

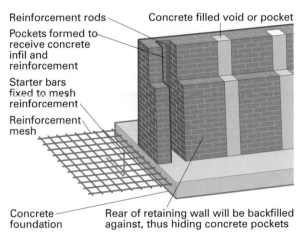

Reinforcement rods

Concrete filled void or pocket

Pockets formed to receive concrete infil and reinforcement

Starter bars fixed to mesh reinforcement

Reinforcement mesh

Concrete foundation

Rear of retaining wall will be backfilled against, thus hiding concrete pockets

**Figure 7.50** Method of pocket reinforced brickwork

## Cavity method

One other method of providing reinforcement in brickwork involves constructing an inner and outer leaf of brickwork with a cavity between them. Reinforcement rods or reinforcement matting are positioned and secured in the cavity, then the cavity is filled with suitable concrete mix.

When building the inner and outer leaves, you must make sure that the cavity is kept clean of mortar droppings – you should apply the same measures you would use when constructing normal cavity walling. Failure to keep the cavity construction clear of mortar will result in a poor bond between the concrete infill and the brickwork.

In some building situations, the inner and outer leaves of brickwork can be built against or around hollow concrete blocks, which replace the need for the cavity to be filled with concrete. Vertical reinforcement rods are positioned in the hollow pockets of the blocks, and these rods are fixed to starter bars incorporated into the foundation concrete.

Mesh reinforcement

Concrete infill

Steel reinforcement starter bars fixed to reinforcement mesh and set in concrete foundations

Outer leaf

Concrete foundation

**Figure 7.51** Typical reinforced cavity structure

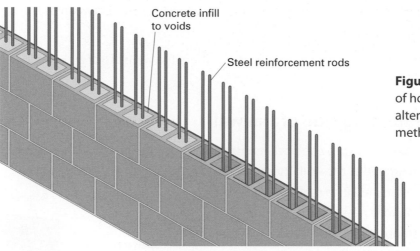

Concrete infill to voids

Steel reinforcement rods

**Figure 7.52** The use of hollow blocks as an alternative to the cavity fill method

## Knowledge refresher

1. Which two bonding arrangements are used in the construction of Quetta bond?

2. What is the purpose of starter bars when placing and securing vertical reinforcement rods?

3. Other than Quetta bond and cavity reinforcement, what other method of providing reinforcement to brickwork structures can be used?

4. What are the limitations of Quetta bond?

## What would you do?

You are constructing a section of walling that incorporates bed joint reinforcement mesh in every third course. You have completed the first five courses and notice that the reinforcement laid at course three is protruding slightly from the bed joint.

What do you do? Do you wait until the work is completed and the mortar joints have fully hardened and then cut off the protruding reinforcement with a bolster chisel? Or do you take off the fourth and fifth courses you have just laid and reposition the reinforcement correctly? What are the issues with each of the alternatives?

# chapter 8

# Fireplaces and flues

## OVERVIEW

In the modern era most houses are heated by central heating installations which do not require a fireplace or chimney. However, it is once again becoming very popular to have a fireplace as a feature in a house and in most cases this can be the selling point of a modern day home. Fireplaces consist of a hearth, breast and flue, with a chimney stack to carry the fumes away from the building. This chapter explains the basic requirements and layouts of the fireplace system and gives examples of the different types of fuels used.

This chapter will cover the following:

- the regulations governing fireplace construction

- the different types of fuel used

- fireplace construction

- the finishes to the chimney breast

- chimney stacks

- the fitting of a hearth and surround.

# The regulations governing fireplace construction

The design and construction of fireplaces are controlled by Part J of the Building Regulations as well as guidance and advice being found in the British Standards 6461. The main areas covered are:

- the installation of chimneys and flues for domestic appliances using solid fuels
- BS 1251 specifications for the installation of open-fireplace components
- BS 1181 the specification for liners and terminals
- Part 1 of the codes of practice for chimneys and flues.

These cover the installation in domestic homes for class 1 appliances with an output up to 45 kW. The regulations are mainly concerned with avoiding the spread of fire to the surrounding areas or structures and the release of combustible material into the atmosphere.

# The different types of fuel used

In almost every home you will find a fireplace, whether it is used to heat the room it is in, or purely as a feature to give an attractive homely feel. As stated previously, the main design is governed by the Building Regulations. However, the type of fuel used will determine the type of flue required in the construction stage or what needs to be installed if there is a change in the type of fuel used for an existing chimney.

There are four main types of fuel used for heating purposes: solid fuel, gas, oil and electric.

## Solid fuel

Solid fuel is the use of wood or coal, or a combination of both. This is normally in the form of an '**open fire**' or it can be a 'wood burning' fire or stove.

## Gas

Gas can be used for central heating purposes and with fires connected to lined flues within the chimney breasts.

## Oil

Oil is mainly used for central heating purposes; it is very rarely used in conjunction with fireplaces.

## Electric

Electricity can be used for central heating. Electric fires can also be fitted to chimney breasts but there is no requirement for a flue as there is no emission of fumes or smoke.

**Definition**

**Open fire** – form of heating contained within a fireplace recess

# Fireplace construction

A typical fireplace consists of:

- a constructional hearth
- a chimney breast with incorporated flue
- a chimney stack.

Figure 8.1 shows how this fits together and names the different parts involved.

## Definitions

There are many names and terms used in the construction of a fireplace. They are listed below so that you can understand their meanings before we go any further.

**Chimney breast** – projection on a wall which encloses a fireplace or flue

**Flue** – a channel or duct leading from a fireplace for smoke or fumes to escape

**Flue liner** – a circular or square liner placed inside a flue to prevent condensation or gases escaping

**Constructional hearth** – a structural hearth or base under a fireplace to prevent fire spreading

**Fireplace opening** – the opening that contains the fire or heating appliance

**British Standard splayed fireplace lintel** – a concrete lintel with a cut out used over fireplace openings

**Gather** – corbelling of brickwork to reduce a fireplace opening to flue size

**Chimney stack** – the brickwork above roof level which contains the flue

**Necking course** – a projecting course of brickwork part way up a chimney stack

**Oversailing** – the projecting brickwork at the top of a chimney stack for weather protection

**Flaunching** – the sloping weathered finish to the top of a chimney stack

**Chimney pot** – the end of the flue, very often tapered to accelerate the escape of gases

**Flashing** – waterproof material (usually lead sheet) used at the joint of a roof and chimney stack

**Midfeathers** – brickwork between flues

**Class 1 appliance** – an appliance not giving an output in excess of 45 kW (an open fire).

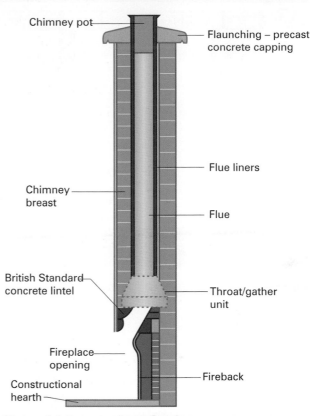

**Figure 8.1** Constructing a fireplace

An external straight cavity wall

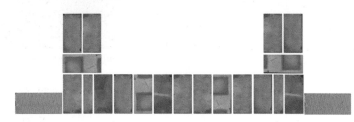

An internal wall

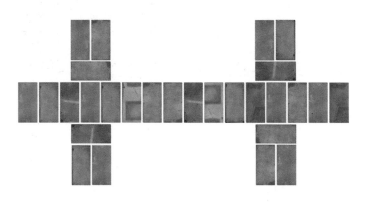

A back-to-back fireplace

A fireplace should be constructed using a brick wall around its entirety to prevent the spread of fire. This can be done using four main methods that comply with the building regulations:

1 in conjunction with an external straight cavity wall

2 with the breast external in a cavity wall

3 in conjunction with an internal wall

4 built as a double breast, back to back.

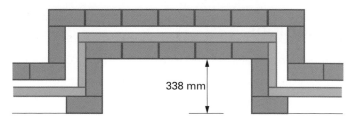

338 mm

**Figure 8.2** The breast external in a cavity wall

More modern or extravagant fireplaces can be built as a corner feature, again using solid brickwork, or circular, self-supporting brickwork, as a central feature to a room.

## The constructional hearth

This is a solid base under a fireplace to prevent the spread of fire. It is made of concrete with a minimum thickness of 125 mm. It must extend fully into the depth of the fire opening as well as projecting a minimum of 500 mm in front of the fireplace jambs. It is also a requirement to extend a minimum of 150 mm either side of the jambs.

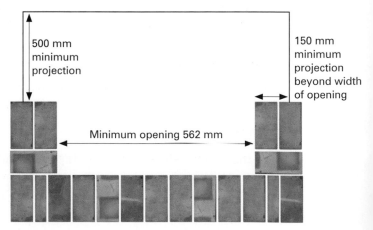

500 mm minimum projection

150 mm minimum projection beyond width of opening

Minimum opening 562 mm

A plan view of a constructional hearth

# Building the chimney breast

The sides or jambs of the chimney breast must be a minimum thickness of 1 brick (200 mm) and extend from the back wall by a minimum of 1½ bricks (338 mm). The width of the opening will depend on whether or not a fitted appliance is to be used but the minimum opening size is 2½ bricks (572 mm). This can allow for a change of appliance being fitted at a later date.

The fire opening must be closed at the top to ensure the appliance is fully encased within the chimney breast. This is done by the use of a splayed reinforced concrete lintel to support the brickwork above. This forms the start of the 'throat' of a chimney.

The internal area of the chimney breast now needs to be closed to form the 'flue'. The flue allows the fumes or smoke to escape into the atmosphere. In older properties, the flue was made by corbelling the brickwork on both sides on the inside of the chimney breast until the flue size (a

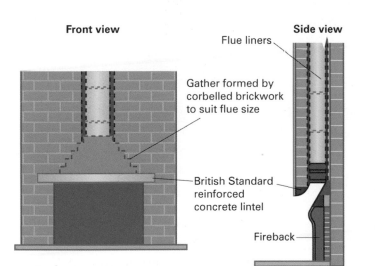

**Figure 8.3** Construction of a fireplace gather using brick corbelling

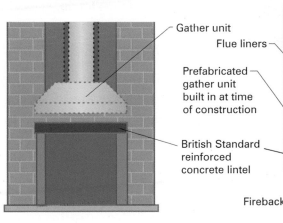

**Figure 8.4** Construction of a fireplace gather using a prefabricated unit

minimum 215 m²) was reached. This is called the 'gather'. The flue was then corbelled forward on one side and corbelled back on the other, keeping the flue size the same, until reaching the side of the breast. This gave the flue an approximate 45° angle within the chimney to help 'draw' or pull the fumes up into the finished flue. Figure 8.3 illustrates this. Once this was achieved, the flue was then built straight to the top. This could also accommodate a possible fireplace in a first floor room above, meaning the flues would run parallel so that only one double chimney stack would be required at the top.

In more modern homes, a prefabricated unit made from fireproof material (normally refactory concrete) is used (see Figure 8.4). This has the gather incorporated within the unit itself. These come in standard sizes to suit different openings as well as different flue sizes and flue shapes to suit what has been specified.

## Flue liners

Flue liners were not really introduced until the 1960s. Up until that point, flues were built square with bricks and the inside of the flue was rendered as it was being built with sand and lime mortar; this was called 'parging' the flue. This was carried out to stop the solid fuel wastes, mainly sulphur, from attacking the bricks. The other problem came from condensation which formed when the hot fumes travelling up the flue met with the cold air from the outside atmosphere. This moisture then ran down the inside of the flue, mixing with the deposited sulphur and forming sulphuric acid and carbonic acid. These could attack the mortar and eventually seep into the bricks and mortar joints. This caused crumbling of the bricks and weakness to the structure, as well as possible staining to internal walls and ceilings. The other problem this could cause is blockage to the flue as a result of parging falling away from the bricks.

The Building Regulations then made the use of liners compulsory to avoid this problem to chimneys in the future.

### *What are flue liners made of?*

Flue liners are made from factory manufactured concrete or clay, both of which are non-combustible and resistant to damage by acid attack. They are either round or square and come in various sizes.

A typical flue liner

### *How do flue liners fit together?*

Flue liners are manufactured with a rebate or socket at one end and a spigot at the other. Thus, when joined to another liner, it forms a perfect seal. These have to be installed the correct way up and the socket/rebated end should always be at the top. This stops any moisture which is

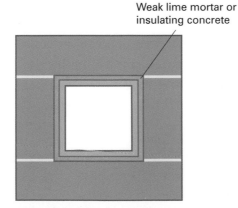

Weak lime mortar or insulating concrete

Plan view of chimney stack

**Figure 8.5** A section of a flue

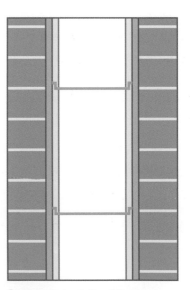

Section through lined flue

running down the inside from penetrating into the surrounding brickwork. The joint between two separate liners should consist of either mortar of the same consistency as the brickwork, or a sulphate-resistant mortar, or a manufacturer's sealant.

All liners should be checked for damage and cracks before using them to avoid problems after construction. The area between the outside of the built-in liner and the brickwork should be filled with a material, allowing the liner to expand without causing damage to the liner or surrounding brickwork. This can either be a weak lime/sand mortar or a weak vermiculite concrete mix.

## Boilers

Boilers are used for heating commercial, industrial and domestic dwellings. The size of boiler required is determined by the **output** needed. Boilers are used to heat water and radiators, so the boiler size is determined by the amount of hot water required and the amount of radiators needed to heat the property.

All boilers should be installed by a specialist registered installer qualified to deal with boilers using the relevant fuel supply:

- gas boiler installers should be CORGI-registered engineers
- oil boiler installers should be OFTEC-registered engineers.

In most cases, boilers installed before 1989 had an output of up to 30 per cent more than was required – a larger drain on the energy supply and on people's finances. Today, more efficiency calculations are usually made in order to establish what size of boiler is needed.

There are several different types of system that incorporate boilers:

- conventional heating systems
- system boiler heating systems
- combi boiler heating systems
- back boiler systems.

Different types of fuels can be used for boilers.

- gas (natural and LPG) – for gas boilers and condensing boilers
- oil – normally requiring a tank to store
- solid fuel – coal, wood, etc.
- electricity – storage heaters and blown-air systems.

Installing or replacing any of these systems will involve a registered installer, but for a solid fuel system, a bricklayer may be required too.

Solid fuel systems come in two different forms: back boilers in chimney breasts and kitchen ranges.

**Remember**

Make sure joints are left flush in the flue to prevent any obstructions.

**Definition**

**Output** – amount of energy (in this case, in the form of heat and hot water) required for the type of use

**Remember**

If you are replacing old equipment or installing new equipment, you will need to know what types of fuel are available in the area.

## Back boilers in chimney breasts

A back boiler is a box unit built into a standard chimney opening to produce hot water for general use and heating through radiators.

This type of boiler has a fireback incorporated within the unit, is positioned onto the back hearth and uses solid fuel. The fire looks just like an ordinary open fire, with a fire grate and hearth, but as well as heating the room, the heat generated is transferred through the fireback to waterpipes connected to the side of the unit, which run through the side of the chimney jamb to the hot water cylinder and radiators.

Back boiler

The top of the 'box' is connected to the existing flue by means of a steel flue section running into the brick flue, or by inserting a stainless steel flue liner the full length of the stack. It has an 'open and close' moving plate at the top for air circulation, so that the fire can be lit initially from the front of the unit. Once the unit has been fitted, the space between the unit and the chimney should be filled with non-combustible material to prevent heat transfer. A solid fuel-type surround is then fitted to the chimney breast to finish as normal.

This type of boiler is mainly used in older houses and does have drawbacks: the pipework connections are difficult to access once installed, and there is unsightly pipework to the cylinder against the outside of the jamb, although this can be boxed in.

Pipes that need to run across floors will need to be laid in ducts below surface level to allow for floor finishes, but will require proper covers to allow future access. The ducts need to be set deep enough to accommodate the pipes required as well as sufficient ventilation and insulation space. This means that the ducts would usually need to be positioned, using timber or polystyrene section placed in the route positions, at the stage of pouring the oversite concrete, normally.

The main problems with this system are that:

- it only works while a fire is burning
- it takes a while to warm up
- replacing the unit is a major task.

This type of system can also be used for gas fire finishes, where a specially fitted back boiler unit connects directly to the fire. Here, the flue should connect to a flexible twin-skinned stainless steel flue liner, running the full length of the chimney stack and sealed correctly to the unit by a specialised installer.

## Kitchen ranges

In older cottage-type dwellings and farmhouses, the kitchen was a major focal point and the warmest room of the house – and this was due in part to the kitchen range.

As with a back boiler, a kitchen range can supply heat to some of the other rooms as well as hot water for the whole house. The old ranges were made of cast iron and had a central solid fuel fire, with either one side oven or twin ovens for cooking or making bread, and cast-iron rings on the top for cooking with pots and pans.

Many larger new homes are now installing modern ranges as a central feature in the kitchen. These do not normally incorporate a back boiler, and can run on solid fuel, gas or electricity.

Kitchen range

# Knowledge refresher

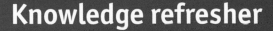

1. What part of the Building Regulations covers chimney work?

2. What are the four main types of fuel used for heating?

3. What is a Class 1 appliance?

4. What is the constructional hearth for?

5. What is the minimum thickness of chimney jambs?

6. What materials are flue liners made of?

7. What two types of heating system run on electricity?

8. With what body does a gas boiler installer have to be registered?

## What would you do?

James is helping to take out and replace a solid fuel back boiler. He has removed the fire surround, and the unit seems to be loose in the opening – he can pull it forward slightly, but it will not come out. What could be the reason?

## The finishes to the chimney breast

As we have already noted, the chimney breast at ground floor level is normally the main feature of the room. Therefore, in most modern homes, great thought will go in to the type of finish to complement the fireplace. In the case of open fires which burn solid fuel, some may have 'face' brickwork specifically designed to a customer's specifications across the whole of the breast. Alternatively, they may have partial brickwork with a '**mantelpiece**' (the rest of the wall having a plaster finish).

Stone could also be used as a chimney breast finish, particularly in areas which have plenty of this natural material.

The finished hearth is positioned, normally using the same material (for example, brick or stone). Again, this is for decorative purposes as well as for protection. In the case of an open fire, it is to avoid hot material having contact with the flooring finish.

In the case of gas appliances, where the fire requires specific sealing requirements, other finishes may be used. These can include timber surrounds with marble hearths and 'back panels' in many colours and designs.

### Definition

**Mantelpiece** – a shelf made of wood, tile, stone or brick to finish the top of a fireplace

### Note

Great care must be taken to protect the finishes until handover to the client.

Fireplace finishes

Older homes have tiled surrounds and hearths fitted and the fitting would take place after the main structure was built. The fitting of this method will be explained at the end of this chapter. It is a basic method for most fireplace opening finishes (other than structural face brick) but other methods may be used depending on the type of fire to be used.

## First floor construction

Once the chimney breast has been built to first floor level, the overall size is reduced to the width of the flue and surrounding brickwork. This is so that it does not take up so much space in the room – it would then have a plastered finish. If a fireplace was to be constructed in the room at first floor level, the construction process would be the same as on the ground floor.

If a chimney breast is built then the reduction will be made at the point the chimney breast reaches the roof space, to start the chimney stack.

## Points to remember

- Make sure the foundations for walls meet correct building regulations and specifications.

- Make sure the construction of the brickwork/blockwork is well-bonded and flushed up in accordance with your drawings and specifications.

- Remember the fireplace must contain the fire or appliance and it must also prevent the fire spreading to other parts of the building.

- The flue must be soundly constructed to enable the smoke and gases to be safely carried away to the outside atmosphere without endangering health.

- It must be remembered that fireplaces and flues are hidden behind finished brickwork or plastered walls, etc. They are extremely difficult to put right if poorly constructed.

# Chimney stacks

A chimney stack is the terminal of the flue or flues. It is very open to the weather so very careful construction is necessary to avoid costly maintenance later. A chimney stack can be very plain or very decorative (this is often seen in older buildings) and can contain one or several flues. The purpose of the stack is the same, whatever the design, and the following points should always be observed.

- As the chimney is one of the most exposed parts of a building, a suitable brick must be used as well as a high standard of workmanship.

- A good chimney pot should be tapered at the top to induce the fumes or smoke to escape and it should be bedded into the brickwork to ensure that it is not likely to be moved by high winds.

- A stack must be high enough to clear the roof to discharge the smoke, etc safely. It should be at a height that does not affect the health of the occupants or present a fire risk.

- A sound waterproofing of the stack is essential to keep out rainwater.

- The flue liners must carry through to the full height of the stack to meet the chimney pot.

- The joint made by the stack and the roof should be water tight. This is done by what is known as flashing, usually formed in lead sheet by a plumber.

- A DPC should be inserted to prevent moisture passing downwards into the building. Lead sheeting can be used (or engineering bricks as an alternative).

## Building the chimney stack

The brickwork and flue should be carried up through the roof space and on to meet the roof. The brickwork should be raised 150 mm or two courses at the front or lowest point of the roof pitch, above the roof.

This is the position where the lead tray should be inserted, to prevent water penetrating down the chimney from saturation of the exposed brickwork above. See Figure 8.6A. The tray should be made of sheet lead and be a minimum of 50 mm wider on each side of the stack size. It should be bedded onto the existing brickwork.

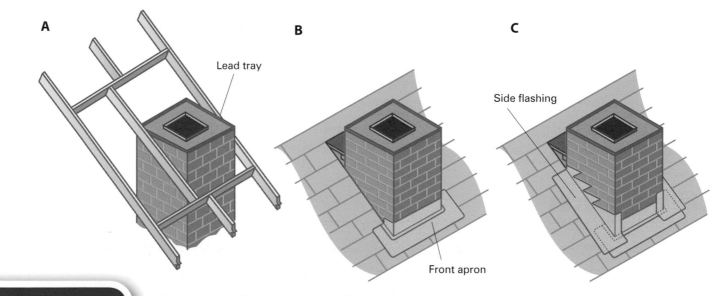

**Figure 8.6** Lead positioning on a chimney stack

The flue area is then cut out smaller by a minimum of 25 mm all round; this is so that the lead can be turned up, in order to stop moisture running down the flue.

The brickwork is then continued to form the exposed stack. The joint under the lead at the front and sides outside the roof should be raked out to a depth of approximately 30 mm for future use. Weep holes are installed on the first course above the lead on the exposed front side. The lead overhanging the stack on the outside should be turned up tight to the stack but, where it is inside the roof, the overhang should be turned down on the front and side areas above the rafter line after the front apron is fitted. This is to force any water that penetrates the stack to run out at the front of the chimney through the weep holes situated in the perp joints. See Figure 8.6B.

The brick joints should be raked out in readiness for the lead flashings to be inserted in order to waterproof the sides and back as the stack is built. See Figure 8.6C.

Once the brickwork has reached a height of 150 mm (two courses) above the roof at the back, a second DPC tray can be fitted and the joint raked out to take the back lead apron. (This is the same operation that was previously carried out with the front apron to prevent water penetration.)

The stack is then built up to the height specified or to Building Regulation heights as shown in Figure 8.7, allowing for oversail courses to be built.

## Oversail courses

Oversailing is the projecting brickwork at the top of a chimney stack which helps to protect the stack from the elements. A minimum of one course is set out overhanging the stack on all sides. The remaining course or courses, depending on the feature at the top, are then completed and the chimney pot is incorporated.

The top is then sealed with mortar raised at the pot edges to allow water to run away from the top. This is called 'flaunching'. The water will then run off the top and past the chimney stack and not down its length.

An alternative finish to the top would be a purpose-made capping made of concrete that is bedded on. It has a central hole to allow the pot or liner to pass through to the required height; this would then be sealed with mortar between the pot and capping.

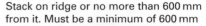
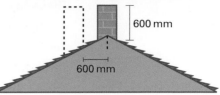
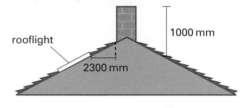

**Figure 8.7** Regulated heights of chimney stacks

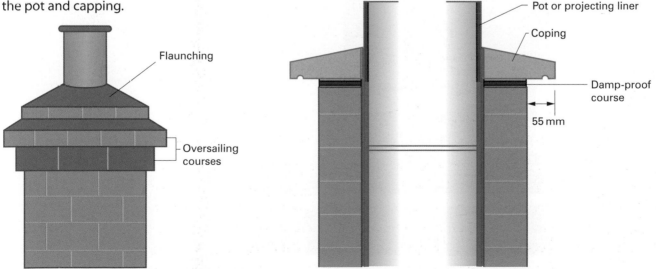

**Figure 8.8** Oversail and flaunching

**Figure 8.9** Concrete capping finish

# Decorative chimney stacks

These days, chimney stacks are usually built to be functional, taking into account costs and using standard materials, so very few new decorative chimneys are built. In addition, many old decorative chimneys have been replaced over the years by modern, traditional stacks. The new stacks tend to use newer, traditional bonds including Flemish and English bonds for stacks of 1-brick thickness or more.

Many old Tudor houses built would have had decorative stacks. Most of those that remain are to be found on buildings that have preservation orders on them, so any work carried out would have to look exactly as when the chimney was first built. As these stacks were built of soft brick and soft mortar, they suffer from weathering and erosion, so restoring a decorative stack takes a lot of time and money. Most old decorative stacks were replaced during Victorian times, and thankfully many still used the same traditional methods and designs.

Most bricks made at this time were to traditional shapes, and as they were soft, they could be cut to most shapes. Some were made in special moulds, sometimes made just for the specific house – in those times, there was an abundance of brickmakers using local materials. However, replacing these stacks today would require extensive photographing of the stack, course by course as it is dismantled, as well as the creation of templates of the shape at each stage. Each sound brick would need to be cleaned and numbered, then placed in padded trays and crates for protection until reuse.

Decorative chimney stacks

New handmade bricks would need to be made well in advance of the work, as they take a long time to produce. Originally, brickmakers cast the bricks in the general shape, then allowed them to dry and harden, and only then cut them to the required shape using a knife. Finally, the bricks were fired in a kiln.

The technique used today follows the Victorian way of production. Textured red bricks are handmade in the traditional manner and fired as oversized blanks, ready for cutting. Templates of the existing bricks and cutting blocks are made for each profile. New bricks are then cut by hand to each required shape and size needed using a bow saw, and rubbed to take out any irregularities and to refine any curves of the profile.

The stack is then rebuilt using the new and old bricks, using the templates and photographs taken as a guide. The bedding and pointing mortars would be analysed and reproduced to match the existing texture, colour and finish as closely as possible.

Bricks are cut using a bow saw

Rebuilt crowns and shafts to the Great Gatehouse chimneys at Hampton Court

A variety of decorative patterns are used at Hampton Court – it has the largest number of decorative chimney stacks in the UK

# The fitting of a hearth and surround

As we have already said, the surround and hearth are fitted after the main construction has taken place. At this point in the construction process, unless the internal brickwork is to be 'faced', the internal opening needs to be finished to take the required appliance.

## Fitting the fireplace

### Stage 1

The first stage is to position the surround close to the opening to avoid excessive lifting, but be careful not to damage the edges of the surround or finished decoration. Measure the chimney breast and mark a centre line with a pencil or a cut line in cement screed. Measure and put a small mark on the centre of the surround on the top edge with a pencil but be careful not to scratch the surround or use a marker that cannot be wiped off easily as this could permanently damage the surround.

### Stage 2

The back hearth within the fireplace opening has to be raised to the thickness of the hearth to allow it to take the fireback. This can be done by using split bricks and then covering with a thickness of sand/lime mortar, or fully with mortar, making sure the finish is level both ways. In some instances, firebricks may be used as the finished back hearth.

### Stage 3

Lift the fireback into place within the opening and set central to the line marked on wall.

**Stage 1** Positioning the surround

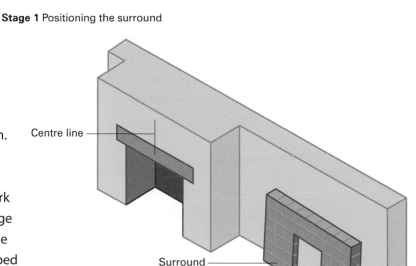

Centre line

Surround

**Stage 2**
Fixing the back hearth

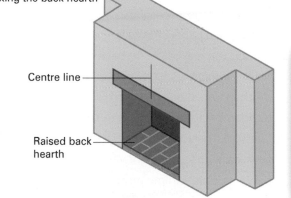

Centre line

Raised back hearth

**Stage 3**
Fixing the fireback

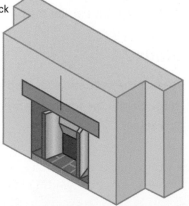

**Figure 8.10** The stages of fitting the hearth and surround

### Note

If the wall has been finish plastered, the area of the fixing lugs should be cut out with a hammer and chisel to allow the fixing to be covered at completion.

**Note**

It is advisable that the rope is one continuous section.

## Stage 4

Reposition the surround and line up the two centre lines. Check and make sure it is level and plumb on the face side. Move the fireback so it is positioned almost against the surround (leaving a gap of approximately 25 mm to allow for the expansion rope). Mark the positions of the fixing plugs on the surround onto the chimney breast wall ready for drilling. Then remove the surround to its resting position.

## Stage 5

Drill the fixing holes using an electric drill or battery operated drill to take red or brown fixing plugs, making sure the depth of the holes are correct. A minimum size of 50 mm screw should be used.

## Stage 6

The next stage is to build in the fireback. Corrugated paper should be positioned around the rear of the fireback to allow for any expansion while in use. The gaps on each side should be filled first with bedded bricks or cut bricks to stop any overspill. The void at the back should then be filled with lightweight vermiculite concrete or sand/lime mortar but make sure if mortar is used it does not push the fireback forward under the pressure.

## Stage 7

Repeat the sequence detailed in stage 6 until the top of the fireback is reached.

**Stage 4** Checking the position of the fireback

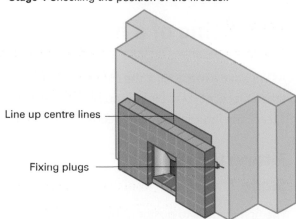

Line up centre lines

Fixing plugs

**Stage 5** Drilling the fixing holes

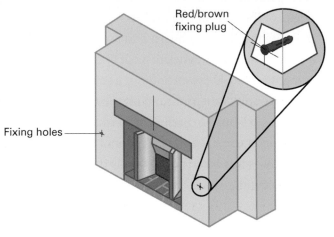

Red/brown fixing plug

Fixing holes

**Stage 6** Building in around the fireback

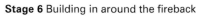

Corrugated paper

Weak fill

**Stage 7** Continue to build up the fireback

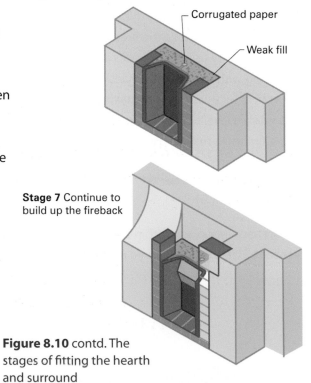

**Figure 8.10** contd. The stages of fitting the hearth and surround

## Stage 8

The space between the top of the fireback and the back wall, a distance of about 100 mm, should now be filled with sand/lime mortar at an angle of approximately 45° to give maximum draw for the smoke and gases to escape.

## Stage 9

Lift the surround into position and line up the centre marks and fixings, level and plumb in position. Next, fit the fire resistant rope into the gap along both sides between the fireback and the surround and across the top between the surround and chimney breast, making sure it is approximately 25 mm behind the face line. Then position the screws into the lugs and tighten until fully secured.

## Stage 10

Bed the hearth into position ensuring it is level both ways and point the gap where the rope is fitted with fire cement to ensure a seal between the surround and fireback. The chimney breast should now be plastered or if this has been carried out, the gap sealed with mastic. Clean off the surround to remove any excess material and protect with paper or bubble wrap on completion.

**Please note:**

Stages 9 and 10 may be done in reverse order depending on the type of hearth used. When stage 10 is carried out first, the bedded hearth must be fully dry to take the weight of the surround.

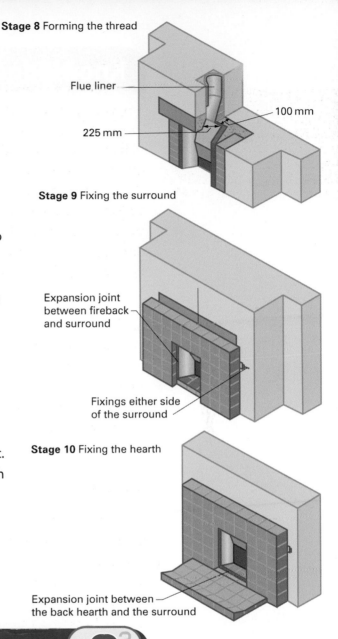

**Stage 8** Forming the thread

Flue liner

100 mm

225 mm

**Stage 9** Fixing the surround

Expansion joint between fireback and surround

Fixings either side of the surround

**Stage 10** Fixing the hearth

Expansion joint between the back hearth and the surround

**Figure 8.10** contd. The stages of fitting the hearth and surround

# FAQ

*What happens if the fireplace finish has not been decided and I obviously have to build the chimney breast to tie into the structural wall as I go?*

This is not a problem. Build as normal and if there is a chance that a full or part brick fireplace may be built, wall ties should be built into the breast and left to tie in the new breast. If this doesn't happen they can be cut off at a later date and plastered over. Just make sure you put in enough ties to start with.

## Knowledge refresher

1. What is a chimney stack?

2. What are flashings used for?

3. Where is a pot positioned?

4. During which period were Tudor stacks mainly replaced?

5. What is used to cut replacement bricks for a chimney stack?

# chapter 9

# Structural and decorative brickwork

## OVERVIEW

The main reason for adding decorative features to a brickwork structure is to enhance the appearance and aesthetic value of a long, flat length of walling. Most of the decorative features incorporated in modern construction projects play no part in providing support to a structure. This chapter deals with the various methods and bonding arrangements that can be used to create these decorative features, in particular the use of decorative panels. Details of the few decorative features that can be used to provide support can be found in Chapter 7: Complex masonry structures on p.174.

Decorative work must be of the highest quality of craftsmanship to achieve the desired effect. Good planning and setting out is essential, as there is very little room for error in decorative brickwork. Materials should also be selected carefully: as the feature in which they will be used is the main focal point for the untrained eye, flawed or sub-standard materials will be all the more visible.

This chapter aims to familiarise you with the different bonding arrangements and the methods used for constructing decorative features.

This chapter will cover:

- recessed and projecting brickwork
- diaper work
- decorative panels.

Decorative brickwork

# Recessed and projecting brickwork

## String courses

String courses are normally introduced towards the top of walls, particularly at eaves level or the last few courses of large boundary walls, as a decorative feature. String courses can be built using a variety of bonding arrangements. These include:

- soldier courses
- dog toothing
- dentil courses.

A dentil course

String courses are sometimes used lower down in the face of the wall as a decorative feature. However, these are more commonly known as 'band courses'. The most common arrangement used for band courses is a soldier course.

String courses can also be formed using specially shaped bricks, of which there are numerous types and variations.

Wherever string courses are constructed above normal 'eye-line' the bricks used in these courses must be lined up along their bottom edge as opposed to the top edge. This ensures that the underneath of the feature, the edge that will be seen, appears straight and seamless.

Dog toothing

Dentil course

## *Soldier courses*

Soldier courses are simply bricks laid on end next to each other. However, unless great care is taken to ensure soldier bricks are laid both plumb and level across the length of the course, the finished article can be unsightly.

When laying soldier courses, a line must be used along the top edge of the soldier course throughout the construction. In addition, a small spirit level or boat level must be used to ensure that the individual soldiers are kept plumb. Just one brick out of plumb will affect the line and result in a poor finish to the feature.

Soldier courses

Soldier courses used as decorative features

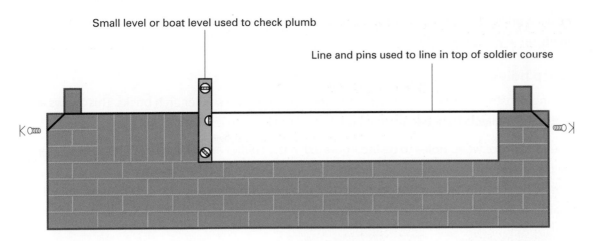

**Figure 9.1** Using a brick line and boat level to construct a soldier course

## Soldier arches

Soldier courses can also be used in the bridging of openings, in the guise of 'soldier arches'. However, a soldier arch is not a normal load-bearing arch construction, and relies on additional load-bearing support systems to carry the soldier bricks, such as steel lintels – or, in masonry clad structures, relies on steel angles or brackets fixed to the structure.

As with all decorative features, soldier arches will be focal points on any

Soldier arch

structure as they are used at very obvious points in a building: above door and window openings. For this reason, it is essential that all the bricks you select for this type of work are of the best quality and are free from any defects, so that they will be pleasing to the eye.

### Constructing a soldier arch supported by a steel lintel

The method of laying the bricks of a soldier arch is the same in principle as that used to construct soldier brick string courses. Once the supporting lintel has been bedded in place, the reveals should be built up to three courses in height, to act as a support for each of the end soldier bricks as they are laid in position.

To ensure cross joints or vertical joints are kept to an even thickness across the span of the soldier arch, a 75 mm-gauge can be marked on the steel lintel. This gauge will need to be modified if the span of the arch does not work to standard gauge, to ensure that full bricks are 'worked in'.

You will need to fit a bricklaying line to run along both the top and bottom edges of the soldier bricks, to make sure they are laid to line and level.

As each brick is laid, it should be plumbed on the inside of the brick with the use of a boat level to ensure it is kept upright.

## Weep holes

During construction, weep holes must be incorporated into soldier arch bricks. This allows any water that collects between the arch bricks and the lintel to escape.

The number of weep holes to be incorporated in the soldier arch will ultimately be governed by the size of the span, but there should be at least two weep holes above any opening. These can be formed either by using purpose-made, plastic weep-hole systems, or by removing the mortar from the bottom third of the soldier brick where the weep hole is to be formed.

## Supporting soldier bricks above openings in masonry clad structures

The illustration below shows one way of supporting a brick soldier arch over a window or door opening in a masonry clad structure. More detailed information on this type of support system can be found on p.349 of *Brickwork NVQ and Technical Certificate Level 2*.

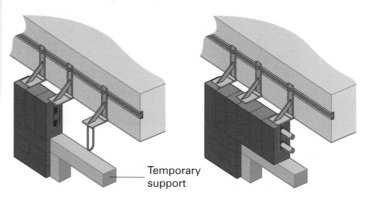

Temporary support

**Figure 9.2** The use of stirrup brackets to suspend brickwork above an opening

# Knowledge refresher

1. Where string courses are used lower down in a structure, what are they more commonly known as?

2. Other than soldier courses and dog toothing, what other bonding arrangement can be used to provide a string course?

3. For what purpose would a boat level be used when laying a soldier course?

4. When laying soldier bricks in a soldier arch, where should you position bricklaying lines?

5. What is the minimum number of weep holes that should be provided throughout the span of a soldier arch?

6. What is the name of the purpose-made brackets used when suspending bricks over an opening in a masonry-clad structure?

# What would you do?

You are constructing a soldier course above a window opening and you have four bricks left to lay. You have been ensuring that all vertical joints between each soldier brick are full and that the surface being placed against the previous brick is fully covered with a 10 mm bed of mortar. However, you realise you only have sufficient mortar left to fully cover the surface of two bricks to form a solid joint.

Do you lay the two bricks with full joints and mix additional mortar for the two remaining bricks? Or do you make the remaining mortar spread for all four bricks by only applying mortar to the edges of each side of the brick, as there are only four to lay?

What are the consequences of both alternatives?

## Dog toothing

Dog toothing refers to a bonding arrangement in which the bricks are laid at a 45° angle to the main face of the wall. This type of bonding arrangement can either project from the main face or can be built flush with the main face. By building the edge of the angled bricks flush with the main wall, a recessed effect will be produced.

When constructing a course of projecting dog toothing the projecting bricks must be lined in by fixing a brick line across the face of the bricks. The brick line will maintain even projection along the length of the feature. The use of a spirit level placed against the underside of the projecting course will ensure the 'seen edge' (the underside edge of the feature) remains straight and even to the eye.

## Dentil courses

A dentil course refers to a string course where alternate headers in the same course are projected from the face of the wall. The same principles apply as for dog toothing when constructing a dentil course in that the underside of the bricks are to be levelled as the work progresses and the brick line is to be fixed across the face of the bricks being laid.

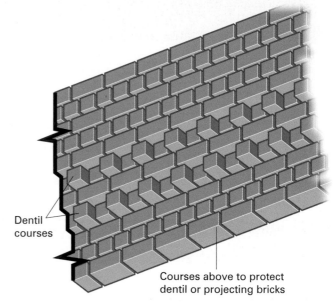

Dentil courses

Courses above to protect dentil or projecting bricks

**Figure 9.3** A dentil course

Both dog toothing and dentil courses should always be finished off with a course of bricks above them. These courses can either be laid flush with the feature course or project out past the feature.

This additional course is intended to finish off the feature and provide protection from the elements and possible damage to face and upper edges of the feature bricks.

# Diaper work

Diaper bond is quite simply the forming of diamond patterns within the face of a length of walling. This type of work provides no more than decorative value to a building.

The diamond patterns are formed using contrasting bricks to those of the main walling and incorporated as recessed, projecting or flush to the face.

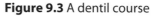

Diaper bond

There are numerous variations to the patterns which can be formed. Normally, patterns are formed using headers, as the use of stretchers is more difficult in relation to maintaining bond and does not provide the same uniformed diamond effect.

Whenever projecting diaper bond is used it is important to remember that all projecting bricks must be plumbed to ensure equal projection throughout the pattern. The projections should be plumbed both on the face and side elevations.

When producing a recessed diaper bond pattern, it is advisable to use a depth gauge or template to ensure that the recess depth is maintained throughout the pattern. These gauges can be made from timber notched to the exact depth required for the recess.

## Knowledge refresher

1. When forming dog toothing, at what angle are bricks laid to the main face of the wall?

2. When constructing dog toothing, how is even projection maintained across the length of the wall?

3. Why should dog toothing and dentil courses be finished off with a course of brickwork above them?

4. What pattern is formed when constructing Diaper bond?

## What would you do?

You are forming a dentil course to the top of a solid wall and only have six projecting bricks left to lay, having already laid 30 projecting bricks, when the bricklaying line fixed across the face of the projecting bricks snaps.

What do you do? Do you repair the line and refix it to the face of the projecting bricks? Or do you leave the line off and judge the alignment of the remaining projecting bricks by eye? What are the consequences of both alternatives?

# Decorative panels

## Types of panel

There are three variations to the way in which decorative panels can be presented. These are:

1  flush with the face

2  recessed

3  projecting.

### Flush with the face

This is where the decorative panel insert is built flush with the face of the main wall.

### Recessed

This is where the decorative panel insert is built back from the face of the main wall.

### Projecting

This is where the decorative panel insert is built projecting out past the face of the main walling. The projection is normally no more than 25 mm.

## Bonding arrangements

There are three main bonding arrangements for use in decorative panels. However, all three have variations.

The three main bonding arrangements are:

1  basket-weave

2  herringbone

3  interlacing.

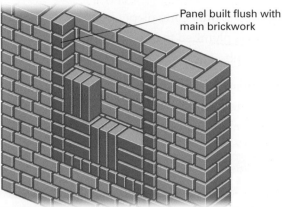

**Figure 9.4** A decorative panel insert built flush with the face of the main wall

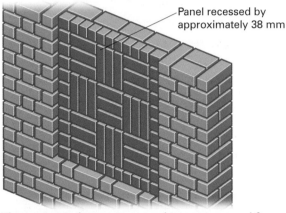

**Figure 9.5** A decorative panel insert recessed from the face of the main wall

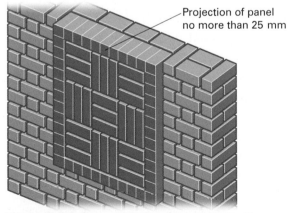

**Figure 9.6** A decorative panel insert projecting past the face of the main wall

## Note

The recessed panel is only recommended for solid wall construction as the panel insert is usually recessed by approximately 38 mm and this would mean that in a cavity wall construction, the cavity width would be reduced due to the bricks being set back in the panel. This removes the minimum cavity width requirement.

## Basket-weave

This is the most straightforward of bonding arrangements as very little setting out is required in comparison to other arrangements used in decorative panels. As you can clearly see from Figure 9.7, basket-weave consists of three stretchers laid on top of each other, followed by three soldiers laid next to them and on top of them.

A variation to basket-weave bond is diagonal basket-weave. This is where the basket-weave arrangement described above is laid at a 45° angle to the base of the panel. This arrangement requires setting out and a large amount of cutting.

When setting the panel out dry, prior to cutting and laying the bricks, further variations to this bond can be formed. One such way is to use one of the main continuous joints as a diagonal joint passing through the centre of the panel in both directions (see Figure 9.9). This will give the impression of a diamond shape in the centre of the panel, which could be further enhanced with the use of coloured mortar around the border of the diamond shape and the bricks within the shape.

Another option is to use the centre of the middle brick of the panel positioned over the point where the 45° diagonal setting out lines cross (see Figure 9.10).

**Did you know?**

Where three stretchers are laid on top of each other, this arrangement is known as 'stack bond'.

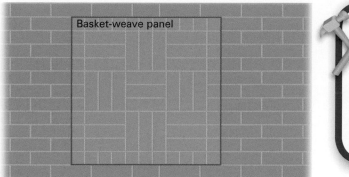

Basket-weave panel

**Figure 9.7** A decorative panel insert in basket-weave

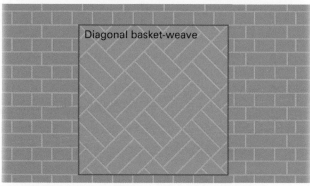

Diagonal basket-weave

**Figure 9.8** A decorative panel insert in diagonal basket-weave

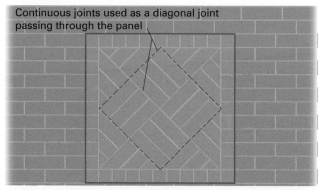

Continuous joints used as a diagonal joint passing through the panel

**Figure 9.9** Continuous joints positioned centrally within a panel to form a diamond shape

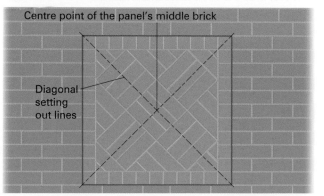

Centre point of the panel's middle brick

Diagonal setting out lines

**Figure 9.10** The centre point of the panel's middle brick is positioned over the point where the diagonal setting out lines cross

## Herringbone

There are three main variations to this type of bond and they are:

1    vertical herringbone

2    horizontal herringbone

3    diagonal herringbone.

All of the above herringbone arrangements have one common factor and that is that the bricks forming the pattern are laid at 90° to each other.

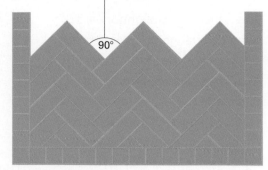

Bricks laid at 90° to each other

**Figure 9.11** Bricks laid at 90° to each other to form herringbone bond

Vertical and horizontal herringbone patterns are also laid at 45° to the base line of the panel.

Diagonal herringbone requires much less cutting than vertical and horizontal, and setting out is also minimal. This is due to the fact that the herringbone pattern is laid in a similar way to basket-weave with bricks laid vertically and horizontally off the base line of the panel and not at 45° as with the other two herringbone variations.

All of the above herringbone arrangements can be built using double bricks as opposed to the standard single brick arrangement. It is not surprising to learn that these are referred to as:

- double vertical herringbone
- double diagonal herringbone bond.
- double horizontal herringbone

**Figure 9.12** Vertical herringbone

**Figure 9.13** Horizontal herringbone

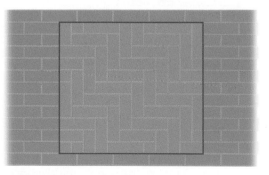

**Figure 9.14** Diagonal herringbone

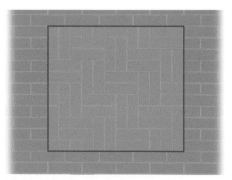

**Figure 9.15** Double diagonal herringbone

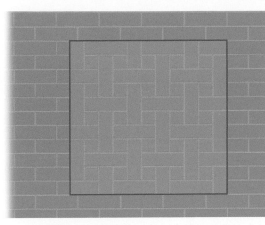

**Figure 9.16** Interlacing bond

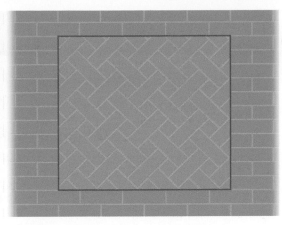

**Figure 9.17** Diagonal interlacing bond

## *Interlacing bond*

As with all of the other bonds mentioned, interlacing bond can also be laid diagonally. The diagonal version of this bond requires more cutting than any of the other bonds.

As you can see from the illustrations above, interlacing bond uses both 1/3 brick cuts and 2/3 brick cuts to achieve the interlacing effect. Diagonal interlacing also has the additional angled cuts around the perimeter of the panel insert.

The interlacing bond is the less commonly used of all decorative panels. This is because of the amount of cuts required which make it time consuming and costly (where the bricks are cut by hand).

## Preparation

For all decorative panels, except basket-weave and interlacing bond, the opening in which the panel insert is to sit should be built first. As basket weave and interlacing bond patterns coincide with brick courses, this type of panel can be built as the work proceeds.

One method of ensuring that the correct opening size is maintained is by using a '**pinch rod**'.

**Find Out**

Are there any other variations or types of bonding arrangements used in decorative feature work which have not been covered in this chapter?

**Note**

When preparing, it is of the utmost importance to ensure that the reveals of the opening are kept plumb and to gauge during construction. If accuracy is not maintained the bonding arrangement will not fit the opening size and will look flawed in its appearance, thus defeating the object of producing a pleasing decorative feature.

**Definition**

**Pinch rod** – a piece of timber cut to the size of the opening and used to measure the distance between the reveals at various stages during their construction.

## Note

If a concrete floor surface is used in step 1 you must ensure that this is an out of the way, unused area. This will prevent the dry bonded panel being disturbed during the setting out and cutting process.

## Note

How the bricks are positioned on the starting point depends upon the bonding arrangement being used. (See the earlier section on bonding arrangements on pages 226–9).

## Good idea

When drawing the vertical and horizontal centre lines onto the chosen surface, make sure that they extend past the outline of the panel. This ensures that, when the panel outline is covered by the dry bonded bricks, the centre lines can still be determined to aid the remainder of the setting out process.

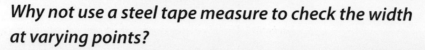

## FAQ

***Why not use a steel tape measure to check the width at varying points?***

There is always a risk of human error when reading the tape measure; a piece of timber cut at the accurate size required cannot be read incorrectly.

## Setting out

As previously stated, basket-weave, diagonal herringbone and double diagonal herringbone are the only bonding arrangements which require little or no setting out prior to laying. However, care must still be taken during construction to ensure that each brick within the panel is laid plumb and to the correct angle.

The setting out process for diagonal basket-weave and herringbone bonding arrangements are much the same.

**Step 1**

Draw the outline of the panel opening on a suitable surface. This surface can be either a flat concrete floor or a piece of sturdy sheet material such as plywood.

At the time of drawing the panel on the flat surface you need to remember to draw the outline 20 mm shorter in its width than the actual opening size. This allows for a 10 mm mortar joint on each side, between the reveal and the panel insert bricks. You also need to deduct 10 mm from the actual height of the opening size to allow for the bed joint.

**Step 2**

With the outline of the panel now drawn you need to mark out centre lines both vertically and horizontally onto the surface (see Figure 9.18).

From these centre lines you must now mark diagonal centre lines at 45° (see Figure 9.19). This provides the starting point for the centre bricks of the panel.

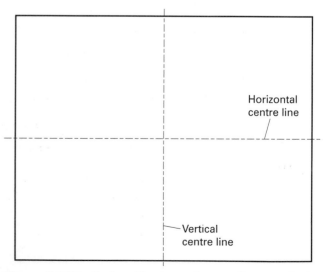

**Figure 9.18** Vertical and horizontal centre lines marked on a panel outline

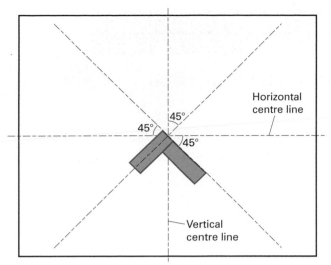

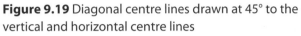

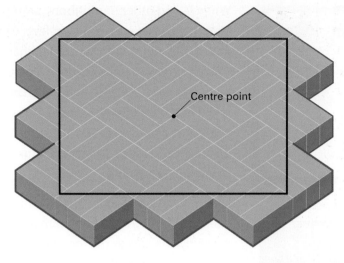

**Figure 9.19** Diagonal centre lines drawn at 45° to the vertical and horizontal centre lines

**Figure 9.20** The panel size drawn on top of the dry bonded bricks

## Step 3

Once the position of the central bricks has been determined, you need to position the remainder of the bricks required to complete the panel. At this point you must ensure that they are laid accurately at the correct angle and with the correct joint thickness between all bricks.

## Step 4

Using the extended vertical and horizontal centre lines as a guide, you must now mark out the panel size, drawn on the flat surface, on top of the dry bonded bricks (see Figure 9.20).

## Step 5

You now need to carry out all the required cutting.

## Construction methods

Ensuring accuracy when laying the first course of cuts at the bottom of the panel is essential in order to maintain the correct angle and gauge.

It is advisable to fix a temporary piece of timber across the face of the main wall, level with the top of the course from which the panel insert will be started.

This temporary piece of timber can be used to mark out the position of each of the cuts, including mortar joints, along the bottom of the panel.

When constructing flush or projecting panel inserts, it is also important to use a line and pins to maintain the face plane of the feature. When building a recessed panel, it is difficult to use a line and pins so a straight edge which has been cut to fit inside the panel recess can be used (see Figure 9.21).

**Note**

In step 3 you are looking to produce the finished effect in terms of appearance. It is only now, prior to cutting, that any flaws or inaccuracies can be put right.

**Safety tip**

If you are using a table type brick cutter or powered brick cutter of any kind you must have been fully trained and deemed competent to use it. Do not change any abrasive cutting wheel unless you have an abrasive wheels certificate. Be safe not sorry!

When laying other herringbone patterns or diagonal basket weave, a boat level with an adjustable **vial** should be used to maintain the required 45° angle of the bricks. It is advisable to check each and every brick is laid at the required 45° angle. This will prevent the pattern of the feature becoming distorted and avoid unnecessary taking down and rebuilding.

Finally, providing the setting out and construction work has been carried out correctly, the cuts at the top of the panel should sit in line with the top of the reveals and there should be no need for further cutting.

All of the bonding arrangements covered within this chapter can be further enhanced in their appearance by introducing a border around the panel insert. This border is normally made up of bricks laid header wise and allowed to project or sit back from the main face wall, in line with the panel insert (see Figure 9.22). The use of coloured mortar in this border will further highlight the feature.

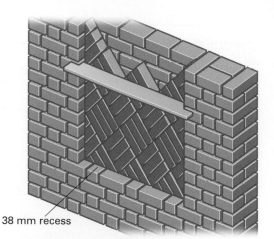

38 mm recess

**Figure 9.21** A straight edge cut to fit the panel recess

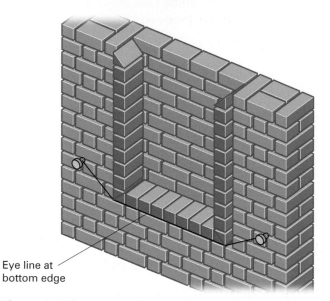

Eye line at bottom edge

**Figure 9.22** A panel insert with a border

# Knowledge refresher

1. Name the three main bonding arrangements used in decorative panels.

2. What is the variation to basket-weave?

3. When setting out any bonding arrangement, on what can the outline of the panel be marked?

4. How much should be deducted from the width of the panel size when marking out for a decorative panel insert?

5. Why should the vertical and horizontal centre lines be extended past the outline of the panel when setting out?

6. At what angle are the diagonal centre lines set out for herringbone bond?

7. Describe basket weave bond.

8. Why is interlacing bond considered costly and time consuming?

# What would you do?

While constructing a decorative panel in vertical herringbone, Vijay, a young apprentice, has noticed that the vertical joint between the reveals and the cuts of the panel insert has begun to widen the higher the work gets. It has been suggested by another apprentice that he alters the remaining cuts to compensate for the wider joint.

What is the possible cause of this and how should it be put right?

# chapter 10

# Repairing and maintaining masonry structures

## OVERVIEW

Some home owners are reluctant to move house and decide to carry out alterations to their home to improve it, either by adding extra space or by changing the current layout of the property. The latter can include taking out walls or putting openings into existing walls to create more space in certain rooms. Home owners may also want to carry out simple repairs or maintenance of a decorative nature or general upkeep of the property.

This chapter will explain the basic ways repairs and maintenance can be carried out and will cover the following:

- adding space to a property

- changing the existing layout

- repairs and maintenance

- material delivery.

# Adding space to a property

There are several ways in which a property can have space added. These could include:

- building an extension to give extra space or an extra room or rooms

- adding a conservatory

- converting roof space (the loft)

- changing the use of a garage or **outbuilding**.

## Extensions

This is where extra space is gained by adding an extra room or rooms to the current structure, whether it is single storey or double storey. If an extension is to be built, planning permission or building regulation approval must be gained from the local council prior to the start of any work.

Foundations must be dug to meet local authority approval, as with any new building with a cavity wall construction.

The external appearance must match that of the existing property, so you must make sure that the brick you use is as close a match as possible. The brick type may be stated in the specification or it may state 'to match existing'. If you are unsure of the type of brick, take a sample to a builders' merchant and ask them if they can either match the brick or tell you what type it is. If it is an older property, the company that made the original bricks may no longer be in production as many of the small independent companies have closed or been swallowed up by the large conglomerates. Some merchants have their own brick libraries showing most of the bricks that are manufactured today which is a great help when choosing the right bricks. You also need to match to the same brick sizes as older properties would have used imperial bricks which are different to the metric sizes produced today.

In addition, all windows must match the existing profiles and materials used (wood or UPVC being the most commonly found, although some properties may have wood frames with aluminium infills). These would generally be stated in the specification for the work or on the drawings supplied.

The extension must be joined correctly to the main structure with the cavity continuous throughout; this process is usually started just below DPC level as the damp course also requires lapping to the existing to prevent moisture rising up at the joining point. The mortar joint at DPC level must be cut out with a brick saw or disc cutter to allow the DPC to be slid into position and the join re-pointed.

Prior to the joining of the DPC, the cavity must be extended. This is done by marking the existing wall at the back of the face brick line and plumbing and marking this line vertically to the height required for joining. From this line the cavity width size is marked and the same process carried out. These two lines are then carefully cut using a disc cutter, ensuring that the material is cut right through to the cavity to ensure less vibration of material at the next stage. The material is then cut out to leave an open cavity which is the size required for the extension.

Now the cavity has been cut, the new external brickwork has to be joined as well as the internal blockwork. This process is carried out by **toothing** the external face brickwork and internal block work.

## Joining the face brickwork

The face brickwork is joined to the existing wall by means of toothing – cutting out brickwork on each course to accommodate the new external wall. The amount to be cut out is determined by the type of bond used on the existing brickwork and the position of the extended wall. If the new wall is built to an existing corner on a stretcher bonded wall (half bond), the half batt remaining from the original cavity cutting is removed, allowing for new brickwork. If the existing wall is built in Flemish or English bond (quarter bond), then the half batt and closer is removed. The toothing will determine the bonding of each course. Therefore, this must be decided at an early stage to ensure that brickwork showing above ground level works to the toothed brickwork for bond or, if this is not possible, suitable cuts are used within the new wall.

If the toothing is to be elsewhere along the wall, then only the width of the brick plus a joint thickness needs to be cut on alternate courses (but you will still need to think about which course to cut out).

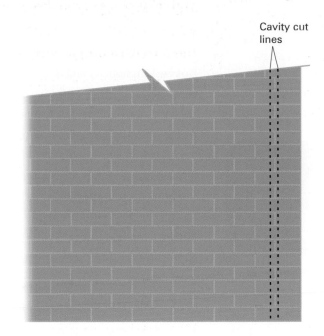

**Figure 10.1** The marking of cavity position

**Definition**

**Toothing** – cutting out existing brickwork to join new

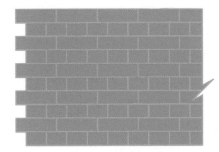

Quarter toothing in English bond

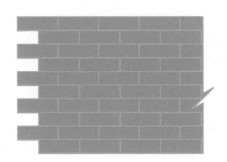

Half bond toothing

**Figure 10.2** Toothing for half and quarter bond

## Cutting the brick toothing

You must take great care not to damage the remaining brickwork around the area when cutting out the brick toothing ready for the new wall. Several methods can be used for cutting but certain factors will determine the best one. If the brickwork is older, with a sand and lime mix, the joints may be fairly soft. Therefore, it may be possible to cut the bed joint with a masonry saw and to tap the brick out carefully. If the joint is made of sand and cement, then a small disc cutter will be required. The cutting must be carried out very carefully so that the surrounding bricks are not damaged – you would need to remove any remaining brickwork if the blade touches it. Chipping bricks is also a hazard whilst carrying out this task. In some instances, a hammer and sharp chisel may be used but, again, great care must be taken not to chip or crack and break the surrounding brickwork. The bricks should be cut by gradually cutting one small section at a time, angling the chisel to cut the middle and back areas first and then the front area so that you don't put too much pressure on the surrounding brickwork.

## The blockwork

The cutting process to accommodate the blockwork is almost the same as for brickwork except that three bricks are cut out each time and the width may vary to suit different thicknesses of blocks. This is aptly called block toothing or block bonding. The toothing must work out to accommodate the block courses so that they line up with the brickwork.

**Note**

With all toothing, always start from the top and work downwards.

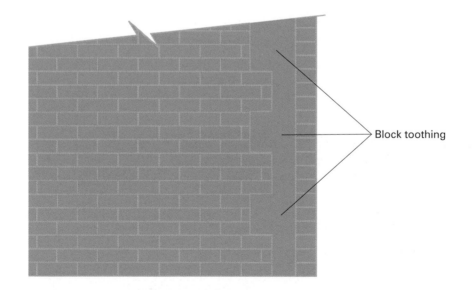

Block toothing

**Figure 10.3** Block toothing

## Alternative joining

In some instances, proprietary wall connectors may be used rather than cutting out the brickwork toothing. There are several different types available from builders' merchants and they can be made of galvanised steel or stainless steel. If used on external walls, only the stainless steel type should be used. They are fixed to the wall by means of coach bolts and wall plugs. Therefore the wall requires drilling, normally with a 10 mm masonry drill.

This system is used because it is quicker to fix than toothing and causes less vibration or damage to the existing brickwork. The cost of buying the connectors then outweighs the time and effort required for toothing. However, permission must be granted before use so look on the drawings to see if they are specified or ask the local authority if they can be used.

## Standard of work

The standard of work should match the existing work so that the joint finish should match as well as the colour of the mortar joint. This could be achieved by producing several different mix proportions in small quantities, leaving them to dry and then choosing the most suitable.

## Knowledge refresher

1. Name two ways to join brickwork on an extension to an existing property.

2. Name two ways a property can gain extra space.

3. When toothing out, where is the best place to start from?

4. Name two ways bricks can be matched.

## What would you do?

You are carrying out some work on a small extension to a domestic property. The specification for the job states that the new brickwork should be toothed into the existing brickwork with matching facing bricks.

A work colleague informs you that they have noticed some proprietary wall connectors in the stores and that these would be a much easier way of doing the job, and would also be a lot quicker. Also, these would also eliminate the possibility of existing bricks being damaged when cutting out the toothing. What do you do? State the reasons for your choice.

# Changing the existing layout

## Forming openings

Altering the inside of a property can give more space to areas which are used more than others. For example, older properties may have a separate lounge and dining area and this can be changed to make one larger room by taking out the adjoining wall, or by forming an opening to allow access from one room to the other. This could also be the case for separate toilet and bathroom areas, or kitchen/diners, or even enlarging bedrooms. The layout is designed to suit the customer but the changes are based on the same construction principles – taking out existing brick or blockwork but at the same time ensuring that the structural stability is not affected.

The same principles apply with all openings: the weight above the opening must be supported by a lintel and the bearing of the lintel must be sufficient to take the weight that has been transferred.

To form any new opening in existing brickwork, the wall above needs to be supported. Checks need to be made to ascertain the extent of the weight to be transferred. The main areas to look at include:

- does the wall continue above on the next floor or, if it is an upstairs room, into the roof space?

- do the ceiling joists above sit onto the wall, transferring the weight of the room's furniture onto the wall?

### *How do we check for this?*

Visual inspection will show if the wall above is load bearing. In the case of a standard size door opening, there will be brickwork in the existing room that will require supporting as well as anything above. If it is impossible to tell then the original drawings with measurements will provide this information.

**Find out**

Find out how loads are calculated and what type of lintels you should use for a specific job.

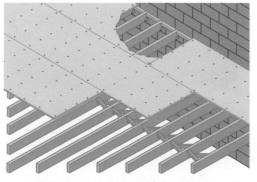

Floor sheeting

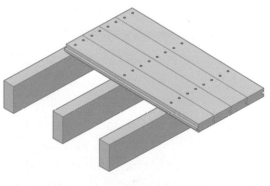

Floor boards

**Figure 10.4** Floorings and fixings

A visual check of the upstairs floorboards will tell you which way the ceiling joists run, as the joists will run the opposite way. If the flooring has been replaced with chipboard sheeting, then the lines of nailing will show the joists. This means that any carpets in the room must be rolled back sufficiently to make the checks.

These checks give us a lot of information about how the weight needs to be temporarily supported whilst the brickwork is removed and the lintel is inserted.

The temporary support system is called dead shoring and is used to carry vertical loads. The system is comprised of props that support timber or steel which are positioned either on both sides of the wall, or through the wall, depending on the way the joists run. The props used to be made of timber but nowadays they are adjustable steel props. These props are adjustable by means of holes and pins similar to trestles and they have a lever screw system to fine adjust for tightening. They also come in different sizes and can be hired from most plant hire companies.

**Note**

Be wary if the flooring has been covered with hardboard as this will be fixed down onto the existing flooring but the fixings could be randomly set giving no indication of the positions of the joists. In this instance, an area of the hardboard will need to be removed to confirm the correct joist positions.

## Positioning of props

Before any work is carried out, all furniture etc. must be moved from the areas so that they are not damaged by the work in progress. Carpets must also be removed or rolled back away from the area and covered. You don't want to incur costly repairs to furniture or carpets which can equal no profit or worse!

When you have found out which way the joists run (see above), you will know how the propping needs to be positioned. There are two different ways to carry out the system based on the way the joists run.

1. parallel to the wall

2. through the wall.

## Parallel to the wall

If the joists run directly into the wall to be worked on, two sets of props will be required, one set each side of the wall. The object of this is to transfer the weight temporarily to carry out the work. The props are placed parallel to the new opening area and need to be set back to allow sufficient space to work – this is to

Adjustable props

ensure that staff don't get injured whilst removing the brickwork and to give sufficient room for working platforms (trestles and boards). Platforms are needed to give enough height to install the lintel when required.

The props should be placed on a scaffold board which must be laid directly onto the floorboards or screed. The scaffold board should be long enough to run past each side of the new opening by at least 1 m. In the case of a standard size door, opening two props each side should be sufficient to carry the weight – they should be positioned no more than 1.5 m apart. A second scaffold board of equal length is to be positioned directly above the floorboard, against the ceiling, with the two props acting as wedges tight between the two boards.

To carry out this operation safely three people will be needed, two to hold and adjust the props and one to hold the board to the ceiling.

The sequence runs as follows:

1. Place the board onto the floorboard or screed, parallel to the wall.

2. Set up the props with the pins roughly in the correct position for the height required.

3. Place the props on the base board and hold in position.

4. Place the second board on top of the two props and temporarily hold from the underside, so as not to trap fingers.

5. Tighten up the props by means of the lever until the board is just about tight to the ceiling.

6. Plumb the props to ensure they are fully upright both ways.

7. Tighten slightly to take up any slack but do not over tighten as you will lift and crack the ceiling line area.

8. Repeat the sequence to the other side of the wall.

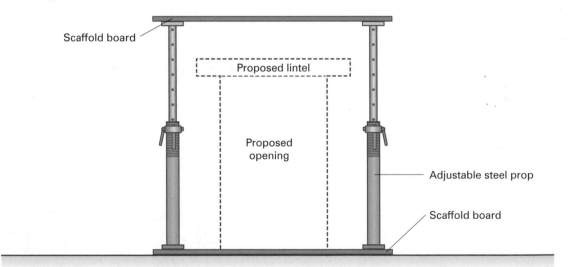

**Figure 10.5** Props in position

## Through the wall

If the joists run parallel to the wall, no weight from the room is being transferred to the wall. The weight that needs to be supported is only above the immediate area so the props are set to carry this weight. Only two props will be needed to carry out this operation and, instead of a ceiling board, a piece of stout timber (150 mm x 100 mm) or small steel (RSJ) about 2 m long will be needed. This is called a 'needle'.

The sequence for the propping is as follows:

1. Mark out the position of the proposed opening on the wall.

2. Mark the lintel position (for this size of opening a standard 100 mm x 65 mm x 1200 mm is adequate) ensuring equal bearings on both ends.

3. Above the lintel line, mark for a hole at the centre of the opening – it must be large enough for the RSJ or timber to go through.

4. Carefully cut the hole through the wall.

5. The needle is then pushed through the hole leaving equal distance on both sides.

6. A base board needs to be set on the floor on both sides of the wall. If the floor is wooden, make sure the base board runs across the joists to transfer any weight.

7. Set up the two props, one on each side of the wall, and adjust the height of the prop to suit the height that the needle comes through the wall.

8. Gently tighten the props until they meet the needle, ensuring that the needle is in a level position. Re-check and adjust the props until the needle is correct.

9. Plumb the props both ways.

10. Finally, tighten both props together so they are firmly in place.

11. Place nails into the prop top and base to stop any movement.

> **Note**
>
> If an RSJ is used as a needle, a timber block needs to be placed between the RSJ and prop to stop any sliding (metal against metal) and for securing the prop.

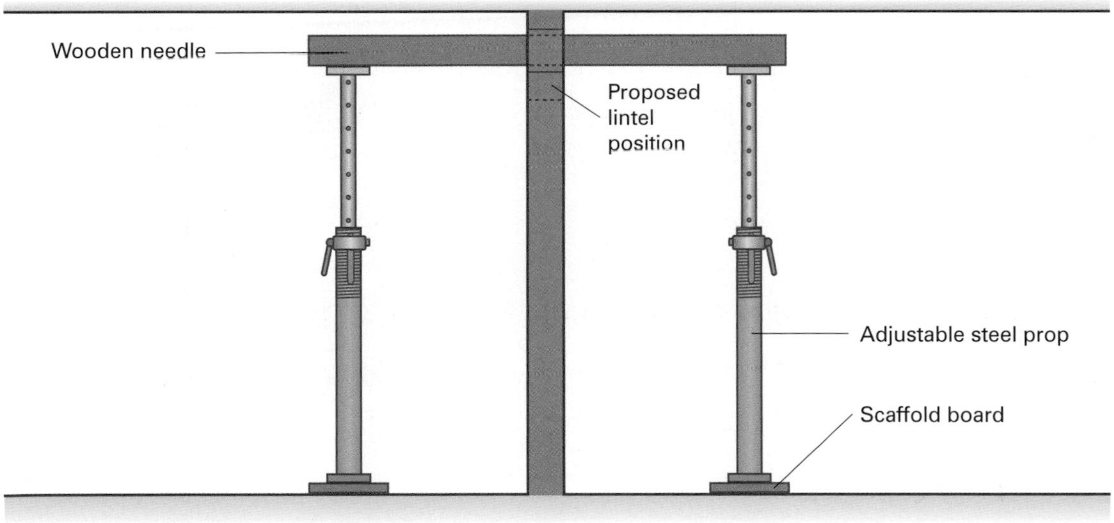

**Figure 10.6** Props and needle through wall

## Knowledge refresher

1. Name three materials that can be used to support an opening.

2. What is the easiest way to check which way joists run?

3. Why should you not overtighten props?

4. What is the name of the temporary support system used when forming an opening?

5. What is the timber or steel called that goes through a wall as a temporary support?

## What would you do?

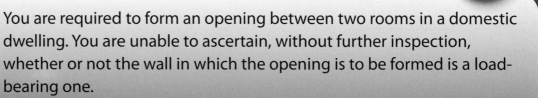

You are required to form an opening between two rooms in a domestic dwelling. You are unable to ascertain, without further inspection, whether or not the wall in which the opening is to be formed is a load-bearing one.

An electrician working on the same job tells you that the wall is not carrying any load and is purely a partition wall, so you do not need to provide support for the floor above, just for the brickwork above the opening.

Taking this advice will save a lot of time, prevent any unnecessary moving of furniture and carpets in the room above, and will remove the possibility of damaging existing floor coverings, such as floor boards.

Do you take the advice given by the electrician? If not, why not? What could the consequences of your decision be?

## Cutting out the opening

Now that the propping is done, you are ready to start the cutting out. The method of cutting is determined by the circumstances of the property. If the property is empty, it may be possible to use a disc cutter (but tape the doors to stop the dust travelling right through the property). Care must be taken when you are doing this as the dust produced (and fumes if you are using a petrol cutter) replace the oxygen within that area, so the correct personal protective equipment must be used with frequent breaks taken outside. This is the quickest method but not always the cheapest as the dust will linger for a very long time. If this method is not appropriate, then the wall needs to be cut with a hammer and bolster. Another way could be to drill lots of holes along the marking out prior to cutting, but this can be time consuming.

The main thing you must take into account is that, whilst cutting the opening, damage to the surrounding wall must be kept to a minimum so you must be very careful. The type of material the wall is made of may work to your advantage – if it is an older property, the internal walls are likely to be made of brick but may have sand/lime joints which will be fairly soft. Newer properties may have lightweight blocks meaning that they will be easier to cut.

## Cutting by hand tools

Carefully take off the skirting board on both sides of the wall and store it for future reinstatement. Always start the cutting from the top – cut away the plasterwork to the marked lines to the whole of the new lintel area. This will expose the material that the wall is made of. Carefully cut a hole using the nearest joint at the top left or right hand corner near to the plumb line. (Do not cut out the lintel bearing at this stage.)

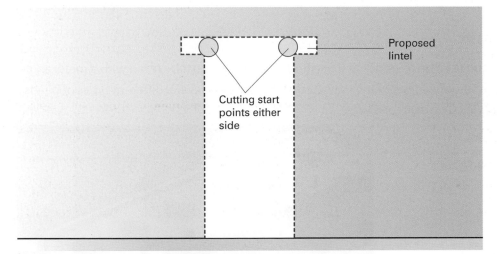

**Figure 10.7** The start point for cutting

If the mortar joint is soft, it may be possible to cut the bed joint right across the top of the proposed lintel first and then cut the brick course out from the bed joint below. If not, the course must be cut out in small sections of brickwork so as not to crack or damage the whole wall. In both cases, cut out full bricks only.

Once you have reached the sides, cut the plumb line vertically with a hammer and bolster. If two people are available, this can be cut simultaneously from both sides reducing vibration and excess damage.

The whole bricks can be cut out course by course. A saw could be used to cut out a soft perp joint each time to make things easier, and the plumb line cut the same as stated until reaching floor level. The brickwork will need to be cut to below the floor level to allow for finishing at a later date.

At this point, carefully cut out the bearings, making sure no damage is done to the course below as this will eventually take the weight from the lintel area.

If the wall is made of insulation blocks, once a hole has been cut it could be cut with a masonry saw down the plumb lines, as well as horizontally, for the lintel and bearings.

The lintel is then bedded into position. At this point don't bed joint the top of the lintel – allow it to set. Once the bed has set, the top joint should be wedged to the existing brickwork with slate all the way along and then pointed. (If the joint is filled at the time of bedding there is a chance of shrinkage of the joint, causing later movement.)

The opening is now ready for finishing.

## Finishing the opening

Any opening can be finished in two different ways:

1    by plastering all the exposed edges

2    by fitting a lining around the edges.

The lining is normally made of timber.

## Plaster finish

If plaster is to be used on all edges as a finish, all the corners must be fitted with a metal angle bead to give a smooth edge to finish the plaster to. There are several different types of beads used in plastering. The main ones are:

• plaster beads

• plasterboard beads

• stop beads.

They all have different uses but produce the same finish, creating an edge to plaster to. Plaster should always be stored in a dry place and used in date order so that it does not harden in the bags before being used.

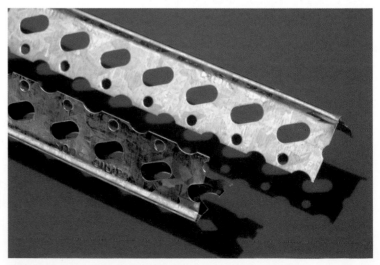

Different types of plaster beads

With the job described here, we will need to use plaster angle beads. These have a galvanised metal edge connected to galvanised wire mesh and are approximately 50 mm wide on each angle. They are fixed into position on the wall by plaster dabs which set quickly to secure them in place. To fix them there must be sufficient brickwork exposed and, as the opening plaster was cut flush, you may need to cut the plaster back about 50 mm to take the angle bead. The corner edge of the bead must be set in line with the existing plaster finish and plumbed on the opening internal edge, allowing for at least 15 mm cover of plaster to the wall. This sequence is carried out to all the edges including the underside of the lintel.

Once all the beads are dry and secured, the plaster can be applied. This is normally in two coats, the first approximately 12 mm thick (but this could depend on the thickness of the existing plaster – it may need to be slightly thicker).

The plaster needs to be applied in thin coats and built up to the required thickness. If sand and cement, or bonding, plaster is used for the first coat, it must be levelled and plumbed using a straight edge or rule. Before the material has set, it should be rubbed over with a wooden float, with nails protruding, to form a key for the finishing plaster. Once dry, the finish plaster is applied and smoothed with a steel plastering trowel. As the plaster dries the surface is slightly dampened with water and re-trowelled to give the finish. The correct timing for this is important to give a smooth sheen to the plaster.

Nowadays, multi-finish plaster is used in most cases. This means that the thickness can be achieved in one coat, gradually building up the thickness as coats are applied and finishing in the same way as previously described.

The floor area where we cut out the bricks now requires finishing with a grit/cement mix of about 1:4 ratio. It must be a minimum of 75 mm thick so that it does not crack and it must be finished smooth to both room levels. DPC may be required below the screed to prevent damp rising. If the finished floor is timber, the boards must be extended between the last joist in each room. You must make sure that the wall below this area does not touch any of the timber as this could cause damp and rot the wood.

When the plaster is dry and the floor is completed, the skirting board can be re-fixed and mitre jointed to the corners on both sides of the wall and through the opening.

Once the plaster is completely dry, i.e. the plaster colour has changed to a very light colour all over, the wall is ready to be painted. A mist coat should be used first as the plaster will draw the paint in, then a minimum of two further coats should be applied.

## Lining finish

Rather than having a full plaster finish to the opening, a timber lining can be fitted in the same way as a standard door lining (the difference is that no door stops are fitted). The lining is fitted by the carpenter and the plaster finished as previously described. Once dry the architrave can be fitted.

**Remember**

Ensure that the beads are parallel on both sides of the wall.

## Larger openings

In the case of larger openings through walls, or complete wall removal, the weight distribution works on the same principles. However, more props need to be used and longer lintels are required. If a whole wall is to be removed, an RSJ/BSB will be needed or very substantially-sized timber, normally oak. This may need to be situated on brick piers to take the weight. In cases like this, you may need a structural engineer to determine the size of steel or timber, and the size of piers if required, plus bearings needed. If a full wall is being removed, the steel or timber is normally situated tight to the ceiling line to give maximum headroom to this area. Once situated, the steel is boxed in and can either be plastered or timber lined to create a timber effect.

### Definition

**BSB** – Btitish Standard Beam

### Remember

Do not forget to place the RSJ/BSB next to the wall before props are positioned, as the props may prevent moving the beam into the correct position once support has been set up.

## Knowledge refresher

1. What are used to form edges ready for plastering?
2. What are the two ways an opening can be finished ready for decoration?
3. What is an advantage of using multi-purpose finish plaster?
4. What type of permanent support is required where the whole wall is to be removed to form an opening?

## What would you do?

You have positioned / bedded a steel lintel above a newly formed opening and you are now ready to fill in the void between the top of the lintel and the brickwork above, which is to be supported by the lintel.

You do not have sufficient packing material, as specified by the architect, to complete the work. The bricklayer you are working with has suggested you use additional mortar to fill the rest of the void, but make sure it is a stronger mix than that used so far.

Do you take this advice? If not, what is your alternative?

# Repairs and maintenance

All properties need repairs as they get older. The life span of some materials runs out and they have to be repaired or replaced. Some areas that involve the bricklayer are:

- pointing
- cracked bricks or blocks (caused by movement)
- damp problems
- lintel problems.

If we break these down we can investigate the causes and the solutions to correct these problems.

## Pointing

The mortar used to build older properties was made up of sand and lime. This is a very soft mortar and, due to weathering or attack, the mortar breaks down. This can happen in small areas or cover whole walls but it needs to be rectified. In *Brickwork Level 2* we explained how to re-point in these situations.

## Cracked or broken bricks

Cracked or broken bricks look unsightly in a wall but what needs to be looked at is the reason why it has happened. If a large area has been affected, it could be due to movement of the building through subsidence, or it may only be a single brick that was cracked when first laid or had a slight flaw which was not noticed originally.

In the case of large areas, investigation needs to be carried out, especially if there is sizeable cracking and gaps in the bricks and mortar joints. Cracks may have small glass plates screwed across them which are then monitored over a set period to see if movement is still happening. These plates are called 'telltales' and they do what they say; some have a measuring gauge to show movement and others may be plain but if movement occurs they will crack.

Structural engineers are generally involved when a large area is affected, so if you are asked to look at a problem like this it is advisable to inform the client of this straightaway. This problem is probably due to movement in the ground causing the concrete foundation to shift, normally through a crack or sheer. The main reason for movement could be due to:

- shrinkage of the ground structure
- tree roots
- leaking or broken pipes.

However, there are other factors that could cause movement such as:

- underground railways
- mining
- ground erosion
- long-term bomb damage.

An expert will find the cause and suggest the best way to repair, normally through underpinning the foundation and rebuilding the wall or walls. Underpinning is carried out by specialised companies to specifications set by a structural engineer, or jointly with an architect.

When just single bricks are the cause of the problem, the remedy is to take them out and replace them. Great care is needed when cutting, as well as when matching the brick and mortar colour and finish. Cut small quantities at a time. Chip away at the brick – don't smash at it – the idea is to take out one brick not 20!

## Damp problems

Damp penetration can be a major problem, causing staining to interior finishes, bubbling of paintwork to walls and even plaster which is powdering and **blown** on walls.

Other areas that can be affected by damp include timber such as floorboards, joists, skirting boards, window frames, fascia and soffit boards which can all rot.

Internal damp is caused in two different ways:

1   moisture travelling horizontally
2   moisture travelling vertically.

### Horizontal moisture

This is normally caused when the cavity is bridged, allowing moisture from the external wall to cross through the cavity into the internal wall. The bridging is usually due to pieces of brick or block dropped down the cavity, either during the original construction or through work carried out at a later time. Mortar bridging the cavity can cause the same problem; this could be caused as explained above or through the breakdown of the material over the course of time, filling the cavity above the DPC and allowing moisture to penetrate across.

How to rectify the problem depends on the area that is affected. If the damp is part way up the wall and affecting a small area, then it could be just a single piece of brick/mortar causing the problem. In some cases, small pieces of timber have been found to be the cause. These will have to be removed by cutting out a brick or two (as previously explained) on the outside wall to investigate – this usually shows the cause. The bridge must then be removed and the bricks replaced.

If the damp is at floor level or just above, the problem could be horizontal or vertical. The cavity could be bridged (as described above) or filled with mortar above the DPC. To rectify this, bricks have to be cut out just above DPC level to see if the cavity is full. If this is the case, then the cavity needs to be fully cleaned to a minimum of 150 mm below DPC level. This may have to be carried out along the whole length of the wall if the findings are bad.

Cleaning out must be done carefully. In some cases, the mortar may be very soft and easy to remove but in others it could be firm and very hard to remove. As the cavity is probably 50 mm wide there is not much room to carry this out. Sometimes tools (basic Neanderthal type!) have to be specially made in order to drag out the mortar.

Obviously you can only clear a small area at a time, due to reach, so more bricks will need to be removed. Make sure when you do this that the holes are positioned so that you can clean both left and right within the cavity as far as you can reach. However, remember the stability of the wall is paramount. Only cut out two to three bricks long per section and leave at least four bricks before cutting the next section. It is advisable to only cut out four sections, if needed, on a wall before reinstatement. When the bricks are put back follow the rules previously explained concerning the type of bricks and mortar and leave the top bed joint out until set, then wedge with slate and point. In some instances, an airbrick may be put in at intervals to allow more ventilation to the cavity to help stop future problems.

Another problem area for horizontal damp is at reveals due to splits or holes in the vertical DPC. In these cases, cut out the brickwork and replace the affected section of DPC, making sure to lap the DPC by a minimum of 100 mm top and bottom.

## Vertical moisture

Vertical problems are normally due to a breakdown of the horizontal DPC, causing moisture to draw up through the ground into the brick or blockwork. If the external DPC is to be replaced, the brickwork is removed in sections in the same way as for cavity cleaning. If the whole wall is to be replaced, it is better to break the sections into four and name them sections A, B, C and D. Cut out all section As first. Lay the new DPC to the cut out opening, allowing for a minimum of 100 mm turn up at each end to allow lapping when those sections are replaced. Replace the brickwork but don't mortar the perp joints against the existing brickwork – wedge

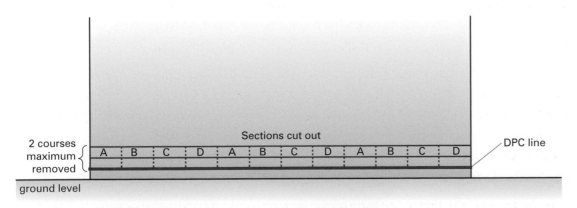

**Figure 10.8** DPC sections

it as described previously. Then replace all section Bs, making sure the DPC is lapped with the previous section. Continue this for the remaining sections until the wall is completely replaced.

If the horizontal DPC has broken down on the internal wall, it is normally rectified by injecting a silicone-based liquid DPC.

The skirting boards and plaster are removed 1 m up from the floor. A series of holes are then drilled into the wall just above the existing DPC. The liquid is then pumped in and absorbed into the bricks. Once dry, the wall is re-plastered with a moisture resistant plaster. Sometimes liquid bitumen or sealer is painted onto the exposed brickwork prior to the plaster to stop any further problems. This work is normally carried out by a specialist company giving a minimum of a 10 year guarantee, but they may require the original plaster to be removed by the contractor.

If damp shows over a lintel, it could mean the cavity is bridged or no DPC tray has been fitted, most likely the latter. Cut out the brickwork in sections as before (probably not as many sections will be required) and clear if bridged, or fit a DPC cavity tray in sections, making allowance for lapping as previously described.

Also available is a plastic tray system, with each tray being two bricks long and having interlocking edges to connect to the next section. It has a flapped back edge which adjusts to meet the internal wall. This stops any moisture which is coming down the cavity from going behind the tray. Obviously, with this system care must be taken with the measuring and placement of further trays, as the trays joining the sections may be too long or too short to fit into their correct position. The bricks are actually bedded into the tray, with plastic weep holes placed in the joint between the two bricks to allow any moisture to run back outside the building. This system is also used for stepped flashings where a pitch roof (for example, that of a garage) meets against the main building.

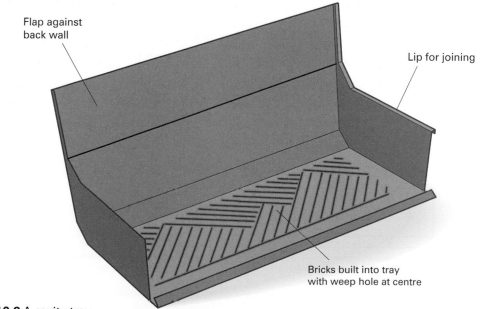

Flap against back wall

Lip for joining

Bricks built into tray with weep hole at centre

**Figure 10.9** A cavity tray

## Damage to lintels or concrete cills

There are two main reasons for repairs to lintels or cills. One is edges breaking away and shear breaks. Lintels and cills are generally made of reinforced concrete. The front edge of a lintel or cill is the most exposed to the elements. Moisture absorbed into the concrete can freeze, causing expansion, or the reinforcement gets damp and rust forms on the steel, which also expands, causing the concrete to break away from the mass. The other reason for repairs to lintels and cills is cracking due to pressure from the weight above or movement around this area.

In the case of expansion, the affected material could be removed, the exposed reinforcing coated with a rust treatment and rendered to finish, depending on the amount of damage. An alternative is to replace the lintel. If the lintel or cill is cracked or broken then this is the only option. The lintel will require dead shoring through the wall and the course of bricks above the lintel cut out. The lintel can then be carefully removed and replaced. A continuous DPC tray should be fitted on top of the lintel and the bricks reinstated, and joint wedged and pointed. Weep holes should be positioned along the line of bricks to allow for any water drainage.

In the case of a cill replacement, care must be taken not to damage the frame. This time the bricks below the cill are removed, taking great care to ensure the cill does not suddenly drop trapping fingers or hands. A section should be cut out at each end under the cill, two courses in depth. Once removed, replace with dry bricks or timber blocks and wedge tight. Remove the rest of the two courses of brickwork below the cill. Slowly take out the wedges and allow the cill to sit on the blocks. Gradually remove the blocks end by end until the cill is clear of the frame. Take out the cill and dispose of it correctly. The new cill should be fitted following the steps to remove the old cill in reverse order. Once in position build back the central brickwork and allow to dry – then wedge. Remove the end wedges and rebuild the remaining brickwork as before.

**Note**

In the case of a boot lintel, both internal and outer skins need to be removed.

**Remember**

This operation should be carried out safely using the correct type of scaffolding to ensure all operatives are not put at risk.

## Material delivery

Most materials are delivered to site on lorries with crane off-loading equipment. This is a quick and efficient method of delivery as the materials can be positioned virtually anywhere they are required on site without having to be manhandled. If the materials are stored in specific areas (this is usual on larger sites), cranes are used to transport material around the site. If the correct procedures are followed, there is little chance of injury to the workforce as no one has to touch the materials. The driver should be fully trained in the use of the equipment, so no other person should attempt to move materials in this way.

In some circumstances when materials are being delivered or moved on site, the driver may have problems seeing the position where the materials are to be placed. In these situations, a banksman is required to give hand signals to the driver to act as his or her eyes. The signals are normally for left, right, up, down and slow movement. The banksman should always stand in full view of the driver and the position the materials are to be moved to, or connected by means of two way radio. He or she should be fully trained in this role and hold an up-to-date relevant certificate.

## Knowledge refresher

1. Give one reason why subsidence may occur in a building.

2. Who would carry out investigations into possible subsidence?

3. What could be the most likely cause of damp appearing over a lintel?

4. How far below DPC should you ensure that a cavity is kept clean?

# What would you do?

1.  You have been asked to replace 6 broken bricks on an external wall to a property that is about 150 years old. Your supervisor has left the materials in the garage. You have cut the bricks out as the joints were quite soft and are now ready to mix the mortar. On reaching the garage, you find the bricks, one bag of cement and one bag of sand. Is this OK?

2.  You are replacing a horizontal damp proof course using a plastic coated flexible DPC. You are aware that the minimum overlap of the DPC should be 100 mm. However, you have come to the end of the roll, and only have sufficient DPC left to give you a 50 mm overlap. The experienced bricklayer you are working with assures you that this will be sufficient and will save you opening a new roll just for an additional 50 mm.

    What do you do? Should you open a new roll to comply with the information on the drawing? Or do you avoid opening a new roll and use what you have left? What are the possible consequences of using a smaller piece than that required?

# Glossary

| | |
|---|---|
| **access** | entrance, a way in |
| **acute angle** | this is an angle less than 90° |
| **amenities** | facilities such as toilets, rest areas, etc. |
| **bearing capacity of the soil** | the load that can be safely carried by the soil without any adverse settlement |
| **blown** | plaster or render no longer adhering to the interior brick or block wall |
| **bridge** | where moisture can be transferred from the outer wall to the inner leaf by material touching the walls |
| **BSB** | British Standard Beam |
| **building regulations** | a set of regulations brought in to deal with poor housing conditions, which now restrict what can be built, how and where |
| **cant** | meaning bevelled, sloped or tilted |
| **carbon footprint** | total amount of $CO_2$ emissions produced by individuals and industry |
| **castellations** | having turrets like a castle |
| **cavity batten** | a timber piece laid in a cavity to prevent mortar droppings falling down the cavity |
| **compression** | being squeezed or squashed together |
| **compressive loads** | loads that bear down on the brickwork |
| **concave** | means rounded inwards |
| **contamination** | when harmful chemicals or substances pollute something (e.g. water) |
| **convex** | means curved outwards |
| **damp proof course (DPC)** | a substance that is used to prevent damp from penetrating a building |

| | |
|---|---|
| **dead load** | the weight of the structure |
| **decibel (dB)** | the standard unit for measuring noise level |
| **discrepancies** | when there is a difference or variation between two things that should be the same |
| **dismantle** | take apart, take down carefully |
| **duration** | how long something goes on |
| **egress** | exit, a way out |
| **electrocution** | death through coming into contact with an electric current |
| **elevation** | refers to a vertical face of a building |
| **embedded energy** | the amount of energy that has been used to create and manufacture the material and transport it to site for inclusion in the structure |
| **employer** | the person or company someone works for |
| **employee** | the person employed by the employer, the member of staff |
| **FENSA** | Fenestration Self-Assessment scheme under which window installers agree to install to certain standards |
| **finite** | a resource that can never be replaced once used |
| **fibreglass** | a material made from glass fibres and a resin that starts in liquid form then hardens to be very strong |
| **foundations** | concrete bases supporting walls |
| **gang-nailed** | galvanised plate with spikes used to secure butt joints |
| **hazardous** | dangerous or unsafe |

| | |
|---|---|
| **Health and Safety Executive (HSE)** | the official body that enforces health and safety legislation |
| **imposed load** | the additional weight/loading that may be placed on the structure itself |
| **inconsistencies** | when things are not the same, not consistent |
| **interim** | in the time between, for the time being, as a holding measure |
| **legislation** | laws or the making of laws |
| **load-bearing** | walls referred to as load-bearing support the load from roofs and floors |
| **making a risk assessment** | measuring the dangers of an activity against the likelihood of accidents taking place |
| **mantelpiece** | a shelf made of wood, tile, stone or brick to finish the top of a fireplace |
| **objectives** | aims, purposes |
| **obligation** | something you have a duty or a responsibility to do |
| **obtuse angle** | this is an angle greater than 90° |
| **omission** | something that has not been done or has been missed out |
| **OPC** | ordinary Portland cement |
| **open fire** | form of heating contained within a fireplace recess |
| **outbuilding** | a shed or storage area connected to the main building |
| **output** | amount of energy (in this case, in the form of heat and hot water) required for the type of use |
| **p.a.r.** | a term used for timber that has been 'planned all round' |
| **penalty clause** | a clause in a contract saying a fine has to be paid, or some other penalty made, if a certain thing happens, e.g. the job overruns |
| **pinch rod** | a piece of timber cut to the size of the opening and used to measure the distance between the reveals at various stages during their construction |
| **PPE** | personal protective equipment, such as gloves, a safety harness or goggles |
| **proactive** | acting in advance, before something happens (e.g. an accident) |
| **prohibition** | a ban, saying something cannot happen or be done |
| **prosecute** | take someone to court for committing a crime |
| **prospective** | likely or possible in the future, but not actually happening or approved now |
| **quoin** | the corner of a wall |
| **'R' value** | the standard way of describing how effective an insulation is. The higher the R-value, the more effective the insulation |
| **RCD** | residual current device, a device that will shut the power down on a piece of electrical equipment if it detects a change in the current, thus preventing electrocution |
| **reactive** | acting after something happens, in response to it |
| **remit** | scope, job, the areas an organisation or individual has to cover |
| **residential** | where people live, rather than a business district, for example |
| **retention** | where the client holds a small percentage of the full payment back for a specified period in case of defects being discovered. |
| **rise** | the distance from the top of the wall plate to the roof's peak |
| **safety policy** | document outlining the company's commitment and stating what they plan to do to ensure that all work is carried out as safely as possible |
| **screeding** | levelling off concrete by adding a final layer |
| **skew back** | the angle at the springing point at which the arch rings will be laid |
| **skew-nailed** | nailed with the nails at an angle |
| **solvent** | a substance that dissolves another e.g. paint stripper |

| | |
|---|---|
| **span** | the distance measured in the direction of the ceiling joists, from the outside of one wall plate to another, known as the overall (O/A) span |
| **sprocket** | a piece of timber bolted to the side of the rafter to reduce the pitch at the eaves |
| **SRC** | sulphate-resistant cement |
| **stipulation** | a condition of an agreement, a particular term of a contract |
| **surveillance** | carefully watching over or keeping an eye on |
| **sustainability** | the ability to last or carry on, how easy something is to keep going |
| **tensile stress** | where lateral loads or forces are imposed on the brickwork structure |
| **tension** | being stretched |
| **tipping** | this is where, if care is not taken during the laying process, the whole corbel may tip forward and quite possibly topple over |
| **toothing** | cutting out existing brickwork to join new |
| **traversing** | means to go over or trace over the face of the arch with the template to ensure the correct shape has been achieved when producing the template |

| | |
|---|---|
| **tusk tenon joint** | a kind of mortice and tenon joint that uses a wedge-shaped key to hold the joint together |
| **'U' values** | a measure of thermal transmittance through a building component, usually a roof, wall, window, door or floor |
| **vial** | a small glass bottle containing the bubble used to give a reading when plumbing or levelling brick or block work |
| **vibration white finger** | condition that can be caused by using vibrating machinery (usually for very long periods of time). The blood supply to the fingers is reduced which causes pain, tingling and sometimes spasms (shaking) should be the same |
| **wall ties** | stainless steel or plastic fixings to tie cavity walls together |
| **window head** | top of a window |

# Index